PREPPING FOR SURVIVAL 2-IN-1 COLLECTION

WHEN CRISIS HITS SUBURBIA + THE PREPPER'S
PANTRY – BUG IN AND PROTECT YOUR FAMILY WHILE
MAINTAINING A HEALTHY DIET AND STRONG
IMMUNE SYSTEM IN ANY DISASTER

TED RILEY

CONTENTS

WHEN CRISIS HITS SUBURBIA
A Modern-Day Prepping Guide to Effectively Bug
in and Protect Your Family Home in a Societal
Collapse

THE PREPPER'S PANTRY

Nutritional Bulk Food Prepping to Maintain a
Healthy Diet and a Strong Immune System to
Survive any Crisis

A Special Gift to My Readers

Included with your purchase of this book is your free
copy of the *Emergency Information Planner*

Follow the link below to receive your copy:
www.tedrileyauthor.com
Or by accessing the QR code:

You can also join our Facebook community **Suburban
Prepping with Ted**, or contact me directly via
ted@tedrileyauthor.com.

WHEN CRISIS HITS SUBURBIA

A MODERN-DAY PREPPING GUIDE TO
EFFECTIVELY BUG IN AND PROTECT YOUR
FAMILY HOME IN A SOCIETAL COLLAPSE

INTRODUCTION

Extinction is the rule. Survival is the exception.

— CARL SAGAN

Your home is your ultimate survival investment. When chaos strikes, and we now know what chaos looks like, your home should be your primary survival shelter. Have you ever thought about your home this way?

These last few months have indeed been an awakening for many Americans. It might be the reason you are here looking over the pages of this book. I am humbled by your decision to use this book as a blueprint for hardening your home and protecting your family from an uncertain future.

Listen! You are more than capable of taking this on. You stand to gain so much by living a more prepared lifestyle. The actions you take are not just about SHTF. You will find that prepping for SHTF adds massive benefits to everyone living in your household. These benefits come from living a life that focuses on self-reliance and independence.

We are going to explore the very core of prepping and give you a clear direction on how you can get from where you are today to a place of preparedness and comfort in your own home. To get to that level, you will be required to bolster preps like food, water, medical, backup energy, and hygiene, and I am going to show you how to do that whether you have a large four-bedroom home or small apartment.

This Is the Knowledge You Can Expect to Gain by Following the Directions Given in This Book:

- You **will** be able to outfit and harden your home for maximum security
- You **will** build and stock a prepper's pantry to ensure your family eats
- You **will** prepare your children and teach them how to react
- You **will** be ready to go off-grid in a disaster
- You **will** have an effective evacuation plan
- You and your family **will** be able to survive the chaos if it comes to your suburb

How do I know all this? If you are going to stake your family's safety and security on it, it is a relevant question to ask.

AUTHOR PROFILE

My name is Ted Riley. I spent my formative years in the scouts, and I still remember getting that first badge for effectively using my pocketknife. I was hooked on the outdoors. Out there, I could swim in the water, build shelters, and start a fire! What more could an outdoorsy kid want?

I spent the weekends fishing with my father, and I learned a lot about woods and waters from him. Catching Summer bass while wading in the cool waters will forever be how I remember my dad.

When I was ten years old, we started moving around the nation and then the world. My dad had an incredibly unique skill set, and he had to travel all over to find and keep work. We didn't want for much as he was well-paid, but we were continually integrating into new environments. Some were safer than others!

We did a stint in Pakistan, and that was an experience I will never forget. The nomadic lifestyle taught me so many things about surviving in new environments. I quickly learned how to be noticed when I needed to be and how to disappear too! These are valuable skills you need to know if you are going to deal with chaos in the suburbs.

This was a radical way to grow up as a kid. In hindsight, it laid the base for my interest in survival and preparedness. The American safety net does not exist around the world. You might get pulled over by cops and forced to give them money. You might have the military come streaming down your street at a moment's notice.

These early life experiences are probably the reason I decided to settle down in Eastern Oklahoma. Here we are, homesteaders, pushing towards self-reliance and independence every day. Part of the motivation was to live a rewarding life where we take part in growing and caring for the food we eat and ensuring we are safe from calamity.

I do not doubt that my family will survive whatever comes our way in the future. We have created an environment that is built around preparedness. This has taken some work, but we are now in a place where every day is a blessing. When the storms of life come for us, we will be prepared.

Before finding my perfect home in Eastern Oklahoma, I spent years studying wilderness and urban survival. It was clear that this was my calling, and I enjoy the opportunity to share my knowledge. This led me to create a Facebook group where like-minded preppers can form a community.

Well, that's my story. Now we need to focus on yours. Are you ready to undertake something different? Are you prepared to face the future with confidence over fear? As I mentioned, I have no doubt you have the skill and the desire to make your preparedness goals a reality.

WHAT WILL BE COVERED IN THIS BOOK

THERE ARE A FEW ESSENTIALS THAT WE WILL BE COVERING IN THIS BOOK. THEY ARE THE FOLLOWING:

Water:

Most disasters do not affect the water system. However, in a societal collapse, we could see the tap run dry. If American taps stop producing water, people will struggle to stay clean, cook, and drink enough water to survive. We are going to talk about building a serious emergency water storage plan to ensure you have access to clean, safe water no matter the situation.

Food:

The more food you have, the better! Of course, it is not just about going out and buying all the food at the supermarket; managing emergency food storage is a process, and it can be one that changes your life and saves you money. This book will help you build a prepper pantry, create long term food storage, and even start growing your food outside!

Medicine:

The average residential medicine cabinet and first aid kits are not of a high standard. Most first aid kits are nothing more than some creams and bandages with a few packs of OTC (over the counter) medications. You can create a serious first aid cache with lifesaving medicines, tools, and skills to go along with it. We will also talk about managing things like prescription medicines in a societal collapse.

Security:

The principles of security are simple to understand. This book will outline how to harden your home and your community by using the concept of Detect, Deter, Defend. If you can affect these three principles, you can keep those around you safe.

Energy:

We are creatures who love energy. We use power every day with all sorts of things and do not even consider it. When the power goes out, it can be fun for a day, at best. After that, things start to get annoying, and then they get worse. There are many backup power solutions out there, and you can outfit your home in several ways.

Hygiene:

Another aspect of daily life we take for granted is personal hygiene. This is one of the reasons that disease and death are not as common as they once were. Personal hygiene preparedness can be handled pretty quickly if you stay ahead of it and access clean water.

Now you know what you are getting yourself into, let's get into it and get you set up!

1

WHEN INSIDE IS BETTER THAN OUTSIDE

KNOWING WHEN AND WHY IT IS TIME TO BUG IN

Unless you are tripping over stacks of money, you will not be able to reproduce the comfort, resources, and security of your home when bugging out. That is the most significant factor in all of this. Your home is more than you give it credit for. We are going to work together to take your home from the good survival investment it is to the ultimate survival paradise.

To best understand the potential of bugging in, we should probably talk for a moment about bugging out. When you bugout, you move from a no longer livable situation to a better, more livable location. One of the biggest hang-ups is deciding when it is time to leave. The best way to deal with this problem is to create triggers.

The use of triggers in survival and prepping is a great way to deal with all kinds of disasters. A simple example of a trigger is your fire alarm, which signals that you need to take action and evacuate your home to be safe. Another great trigger is the tornado warning. It tells you that you need to shelter-in-place away from windows, at the center of your home, or in a basement.

When it comes to the bugout, there are some very simple triggers that you can easily remember using the acronym REDOUT.

- **R**esources
- **E**nvironment
- **D**estination
- **O**verwhelming Force
- **U**npreparedness
- **T**hreat Increases

These triggers tell you it is time to bug out because your community is no longer safe for you and your family. Each trigger is unique but presents a serious threat.

Resources: There may not be enough resources available in your area, such as gasoline, food, medical help, and water.

Environment: Something like a nuclear meltdown or serious hurricane could create an environment that is dangerous to your health if you stay there.

Destination: While leaving your home for that bugout location might sound like a good move, you need to have an alternative destination. If you and your family bugout without a destination, you could do yourselves more harm than good.

Overwhelming Force: There could come a time when a riot or military or terrorist presence reaches your area and represents a force you cannot withstand. It is time for a strategic retreat.

Unpreparedness: You could face a threat you have not considered and therefore are not adequately prepared to withstand. This can happen to seasoned preppers. Sometimes something just pops up out of nowhere.

Threat Increases: While you might be managing your bug in just fine, the threat outside your home could increase to the point that it is no longer safe.

These are all serious situations that come with the risk of leaving your home and traveling to a new location amid chaos.

SO, WHAT DO I TAKE WITH ME ON A BUGOUT?

Building a bug-out bag to carry on your trip is a very personal undertaking. It is not as simple as just piling some of the most popular survival tools into a bag and ensuring it is filled to the brim. You have to first understand your bugout plan and location so you can know what you need in your bugout bag.

If your entire trip is 30 miles and you are taking that journey by car, there is no need to pack your bug-out bag with all sorts of water, food, and tools for building a wilderness shelter. If you are driving from point A to point B, you can pack pretty light.

Bugout shelters and sleep systems are a big deal. Building survival shelters is another exciting task that many people spend a lot of time on. Does your bugout require a shelter or a sleep system? Do you need a tent or a hammock?

We will go over some essential items that all bugout bags would benefit from. However, you should not assemble a bug-out bag until you have established a bugout location and route. These two plans will change everything, including how much and what type of equipment you bring as well as how you choose to carry all your preps.

Pump Water Filter:

While you might see straw-style filters and like the look of them, you can only use them at a water source. However, a pump filter allows you to fill containers or bladders so you can drink and travel. You will not always be able to find a body of water when you want a drink.

Self Defense:

If you are leaving your home because of chaos, it is vital to have a firearm or other means of defending yourself.

Seasonal Clothing:

Dressing for the weather is critical. You need to be warm when it is cold and cool when it is hot. Underestimating the elements will put a stop to a bugout, no matter how badly you need to get away.

Rain Gear:

When it rains, you have to stay dry. Moisture causes all kinds of problems, from skin damage to hypothermia.

Sunscreen:

While not a very cool bugout tool, sunscreen will protect you from discomfort. The sun can be brutal in a bug out situation.

Bug Spray:

Mosquitoes, mites, and other bugs can present a world of discomfort, just like the sun. Again, this is not a cool multi-tool, but it is a beneficial one.

Maps:

Paper maps are essential when you are on the road and bugging out. You could encounter any number of obstacles. Detours may happen several times, and you might not have the internet to automatically take you to your next detour.

Compass:

If you carry a map, you should also carry a compass and know how to use it.

Radios:

Communication is fundamental during a bugout. You might have a caravan of cars, or you might get separated into groups on foot. Radios will allow you to keep in contact despite the situation.

Flashlight:

You do not get to choose when the bugout takes place. If you did, it would be in spring when the weather is excellent. However, it could happen in the winter or in the dark, and you will need to have light.

The bugout should be your last resort, and you should focus your money, time, and effort on creating a serious survival headquarters in your home.

BUILDING A SURVIVAL HEADQUARTERS

While the situations above can incite fear and push you to the more radical fringes of prepping, remember that most disasters and emergencies will be dealt with from the safety of your home. That is where your support should be. If you dedicate yourself to creating a survival headquarters capable of weathering a societal collapse, you could avoid the risky bugout altogether.

More good news: preparing your suburban survival headquarters is not as lofty a goal as you might think. Most of the resources and skills you need can be acquired over time. You do not need to make a significant investment. If you can touch on each of these key survival priorities, week by week, you will start to see your level of preparedness improve, and your readiness take shape. Remember, this is a lifestyle of preparedness and not a one-time trip to the shops after which you store your purchases in the basement to be forgotten.

Water: You need 1-3 gallons of fresh water per person per day for drinking, cleaning, and washing.

Food: You need 2,000 (at minimum) calories per person per day.

Medicine: You need backups of prescription medicines and OTC medicine stockpiles along with skills and knowledge for treating illness and injury.

Security: You need to understand three security principles: Detect, Deter, Defend.

Energy: You need to be able to charge essential electronics, cook, and regulate the temperature of your environment.

Hygiene: You need to be able to store essential hygiene items and may even learn how to make some!

Reading this book and being proactive will make all of the above possible. By developing these survival priorities, you will be more prepared to bug in during an emergency. These resources are crucial not only from a preparedness standpoint but also because these are the reasons people leave an area. Remember, the R in REDOUT is resources.

While not all disasters and emergencies will allow you to stay at home and bug in, many do. There are numerous benefits to facing off against a disaster in the comfort of your own home. If we are honest, these benefits far outweigh those you might have in a bugout situation.

Here are Just a Few of the Benefits That Go Along With Bugging in Rather Than Bugging Out:

- Unless any of your priorities are under threat, home is the safest place for your family in most disasters.
- A well-stocked home provides shelter, safety, and all the essentials you need to survive.
- Staying home provides a sense of normalcy, which is particularly valuable if you have children.
- It is easier to get quality sleep at home (which can't be underestimated in a societal collapse).
- It is easier to detect threats at home.

- Home offers the advantage of community relationships.
- When you are at home, your family knows where to find you.

Transforming your home into an effective survival headquarters, designed for a long-term bugin, is the goal. Of course, disaster could strike while you are at work or away from home. You could be forced to shelter-in-place at work due to some nuclear, biological, or chemical attack or emergency.

In this case, you will want to have a means of getting home if possible. This might require something like the construction of a get home bag (GHB). This bag stays in your car, and its sole purpose is to get you home safely in an emergency. When cars are not allowed on the road or threats have become severe along your route home, this bag should allow you to drive, ride, or walk home.

Most importantly, the decision to bug in, get home, or bug out should be based on good information. Multiple sources of information are best when you are deciding to make a life-changing decision like this one. Outside of news sources, there are ways to listen to police and fire scanners that can give you on the ground intelligence which will shape your reaction. If you can stay ahead of the herd, you will be set up for success.

School lockdowns can also be a big problem when you need to react quickly to a disaster. You will need to get the family together whether you plan to bug out or bug in. It is helpful to establish a meeting place if all hell breaks loose. This should be a safe and secure area where you can find your kids and know they will be safe regardless of the situation.

The tremendous benefits and practicality of bugging in are why you should focus on it as the nucleus of your emergency preparedness planning. The need to bug out may arise, and we will touch on that in chapter 10, but the focus on building your survival headquarters at home should be what moves the needle. Suburban prepping is definitely about resources, but community resources will be the most effective. You lose these resources when you isolate and bug out to the woods.

KEY CHAPTER CONCEPTS

- Your home is your greatest survival shelter.
- A well-stocked and organized home is a prepared home.
- Treat your home as a survival headquarters.

2

EMERGENCY PREPAREDNESS BASICS

CRITICAL INFORMATION AND ORGANIZATION

When you see civil unrest on the news and feel that sensation of fear and desperation, it is easy to go right into buying. Buying food, water, guns, ammo, hygiene products can make you feel much better about where you stand in the world. If you take this path, you will find yourself panic buying or buying things you might not need in large quantities. You do not need everything right away, and if you begin to panic buy, this can become very costly.

Many preppers from my community have shared stories of their terrible decisions to purchase bulk items all at once. Usually, they find that they do not know how to use the equipment, do not like the food they have bought, or regret their purchases because their finances suffered due to their panic.

One case in particular sticks out more than most; it is the story of a young classically-trained chef who understood food better than most of the population. He used ingredients I had never heard of before and worked in some of the nation's best restaurants. His trip into preparedness had him reading all kinds of blogs and post-apocalyptic fiction. This chef's forays into the world of prepping had convinced him that he needed to store hard red wheat. This was the one ingredient he hadn't worked with, but he panicked and bought a lot of it!

Long story short, he realized he should have had a plan, and he should have stocked up on the foods he and his family ate every day. That is the power of fear. It can make you do things you would not normally consider. So how do you make sure that you do not get swept up in the waves of fear? Well, the greatest enemy of fear is planning, so you are going to create and refine your ERP (Emergency Response Plan).

YOUR ERP

Written plans are one of the most powerful preparedness tools you can create. They are often overshadowed by the allure of gadgets, guns, and body armor. When you are testing new gear, you feel a lot cooler than when you are sitting around with glasses on writing up your evacuation plan.

However, your ERP is one of the most important preps you will undertake. Not only does it offer up clear steps for when disaster strikes, but it also gives your family an invaluable tool if you are not around.

The fact that you are reading this book means that you are likely the head of preparedness in your household or you plan to be. The head of the household's biggest mistake is to run their home like a military operation and not share their knowledge, plans, skills, and training with the other members. If you were lost to the chaos, what would your family do? Would anyone be equipped to take up the reins and be effective? To successfully protect yourself and your family, everyone must be able to, to some degree, manage without you.

You have a lot of knowledge and information in your head that your spouse and kids may not. The Emergency Response Plan offers your family a means to survive by understanding the step-by-step plans they need to take in several disasters and emergencies. You could also include survival guides, first aid information, and other essential documents in your ERP.

Depending on how much you enjoy writing, the Emergency Response Plan may be a fun weekend or a nightmare; regardless, it must be done! You could use a simple freelance writer to put together your ERP if you do not feel confident writing your own. Of course, this presents many issues if you are tight on OPSEC (operational security). Even if you hate the idea of sitting down and writing, take the time. It will make a huge difference.

ERP Layout

The layout of your ERP is vital so that you can help your family navigate the document's innards. Your ERP may have 50 pages of information, and your family will only be accessing this ERP in the worst-case scenario. They may not have tons of time to leaf through your creation. This is why I like to take my time with it and show my family each section I either include, modify, or remove from our ERP. By doing it step by step, you give your family the best possible chance to understand both the layout and your thinking. Having an ERP night where you spend hours filling your family's heads with information that they will most likely forget is not the most effective way to introduce them to the plan. By doing it step-by-step, your family may have ideas and solutions to problems you have not considered. Adding in their ideas helps create a family unit and validates every family member you aim to protect.

Example: An emergency alert buzzes on your phone, and you find out that a nuclear power plant, of which there are 99 across the nation, has had an accident and resulted in a nuclear meltdown that may or may not affect your area. If you are at work, your family will want to know how to respond. An index or a tab, or both, will give you quick access to the Nuclear Emergency Plan.

Plans like these are not something we can expect our family just to have logged in the back of their mind. Let's look at the basic layout of a sample ERP. Remember, you can craft this any way you see fit. Just keep remembering that it should be easily accessible.

Location of Emergency and Disaster Essentials:

- Blackout kit
- First aid kits
- Fire extinguishers

List of Important Numbers for Emergencies:

These numbers should be neighbors, emergency services, family members, and anyone else who could be an ally or essential service in a disaster or emergency. You may already have these on your phone. However, if your phone is compromised, is it wise to have a backup, hard-copy available.

- Family and Friends
- Phone Contact Trees for Schools and Organizations
- Business Contacts
- Day Care
- Kid's Schools

- Kid's Friends and Families
- Doctors and Specialists
- Work Numbers
- Non-Emergency
- Utilities

Fire Drill:

Your fire drill is something that should be practiced regularly. This drill will dictate how your family deals with a fire in real-time. The fire drill should be tailored to the specific layout of your location. However, the following well-known sequence is a tried and proven drill that can be adapted as required.

- Stop
- Drop
- Roll

Shelter-in-Place:

There are many reasons your family might need to shelter-in-place. You should identify a location and pile everyone inside to ensure it is a good fit. Do not forget your pets!

Evacuation:

Sometimes you just have to go. Evacuation is quite different from a bug out, but we will get to that later. However, evacuation is important. Sometimes anarchy can be avoided by going to stay with some family for a few days.

Regional Preparedness Plans:

Every region has unique threats, and these threats need to be addressed in your ERP. Hurricanes, Wildfires, and Earthquakes are just some examples.

Bugout Plan:

The bugout plan is a serious undertaking. If you take the time and invest the money in executing a bugout plan, be sure you document everything.

Base Defense Plan:

Now, more than ever before, it is easy to understand the importance of securing your neighborhood. A base defense plan is used to create a perimeter and other important locations around your area.

Basic First Aid Resource:

There are a lot of first aid kits for sale. You can go to any drug store or chain store and find a few varieties. Some of the best kits at places like Target and Walmart include merely a few types of bandanas, cold compress, tweezers, ACE bandages, some creams, maybe a few bandages, and minimal OTC meds. If you are going to be medically prepared, you need to create a first aid cache.

Caching first aid supplies is a crucial part of preparedness. The problem is most Americans do not have a good understanding of basic first aid and treating people who are wounded, so they buy the kit, and most never open it or explore it! You need to add to your first aid cache some very important things, but you also need to know how to use them.

The modern first aid kit does not put anything in the kit that could potentially cause harm. Sometimes you need something like a tourniquet, which could potentially cause harm if left on too long. Sometimes you need something like a decompression needle to drain the blood from a punctured lung.

You should not invest in this type of equipment if you do not know how to use it. Therein lies the problem when it comes to first aid in the average person's home. We do not practice any kind of first aid or train it or learn it! What's even worse is the fact that your community offers CERT training at least once a year, and you can learn all of your first aid basics, but many people don't take this opportunity.

There are also higher-level first aid and trauma courses around the nation that are popping up more and more. These are an investment, but you will learn how to use things like chest seals, tourniquets, and decompression needles. These are lifesaving tools, but you need to know how to use them and understand that some can do more harm than good in the untrained hands.

You should also have access to a decent first aid manual. It does not have to be a MERCK, but it should be a comprehensive guide to dealing with injuries and trauma. CPR, Shock, breaks, sprains, and the like should all be addressed in the manual you choose. The reason for a small manual is so that you can stuff it down into your cache. When you build your first aid cache, it should be a one-stop-shop for everything you need.

Start with a medium to large-sized Rubbermaid container. This container should be able to fit the full scale of your most important, in-home, first aid items.

What Goes Into a First Aid Cache?

- Any previously purchased first aid kits
- OTC meds that your family uses and might need
- Thermometers
- Electrolyte Powders
- Rolled Gauze
- Nitrile Gloves
- Medical Tape
- Shears
- Peroxide
- Neosporin
- Rubbing Alcohol
- A variety of bandages with a focus on 5x9s

- Israeli Pressure Bandages
- QuikClot Gauze
- N95 Masks
- We also keep an essential oils kit

This is the making of a serious survival cache for your home. This is a container that you can grab and throw in a car if you need to bug out but can also be brought to a victim in need of treatment. If you are busy rifling through a closet or struggling to find what you need in your medicine cabinet, it could take away from precious time.

In many emergencies and disasters, the first responders are simply overwhelmed. We have seen this during the pandemic. This means you and yours might become the medical staff. Are you prepared for that?

- Prescriptions
- Blood Types
- Pre-existing Conditions
- Allergies
- Previous Severe Injuries
- Doctors Contact Information

These are all examples of vital documentation that you need to have on hand in an emergency. Each of your family members should have a card with this information on it. This will save medical staff precious time in the event of an injury sustained during a disaster. You will also be able to refer to this information yourself if you become the one treating the person you love most!

We will dig deeper into medical preparedness in our later chapter on the topic, but understanding and caching medical supplies and information is essential for good organization and efficiency.

Vital Documentation:

Whether you know it or not, there is a collection of documentation that proves you are who you are, and you own what you own. We rarely use this kind of documentation, but you will need all of your important information in the event of some serious collapse. You may have to prove who you are and what belongs to you at a moment's notice. You might have to prove that your children are truly yours!

Having this documentation or copies of it is a powerful first step in reacting to a disaster. If you have to leave your home in a hurry, this is the type of information that you need to have on hand. If your home is washed away by flooding water or torn down by civil unrest, the recovery will be much easier if you have all your important documentation.

Proof and Legality Documentation:

- Licenses
- Social Security Information
- Military Record
- Birth Certificates for ALL family members
- Immigration Records
- Adoptions Records
- Credit Card Info

Medical Information and Documentation:

- Immunizations
- Medical History
- Prescriptions
- Insurance Information

Insurance Documentation:

- Insurance Policy
- Local Agency Office
- Insurance Cards
- Home Inventory of Valuables

You could also gather together legal documents like your power of attorney information. A small document safe is the best location for these copies unless you have copies of your emergency response plan. Then you have it all in a one-stop location. I like the safe because you can store things like cash, silver, gold, ammunition, and even a firearm safely, and in the event of an emergency, you can grab it and go!

A simple thumb drive filled with digital copies of these documents is an excellent backup in case something were to happen, and you no longer had access to the hard copies or if you didn't want to turn over an original to someone you didn't trust. The thumb drive can be loaded with survival information, too! You can build a de facto survival thumb drive in an afternoon.

No matter where you decide to store your vital documents and backup copies, just know that this puts you one step ahead in how you react to the chaos in your community. The speed of your reaction will make all the difference if you are trying to stay ahead of crowds and calamity.

Checklists and Organization:

If you do not know what you have, you can never know what you need! The point of checklists is not about defining what you need but understanding the gaps in what you have. If you look at checklists to buy more things, then a checklist will be longer than it needs to be and wind up costing you significantly more than you need to spend.

Your checklists should also be uniquely yours. While using a basic checklist to start is fine, you should modify that list to add the items that are important to you. Keeping your preps organized is another key to your preparedness success. Just imagine that you are forced out of your home by a disaster or emergency. You are going to want to take as many of your preps as you can fit, right? Organized tubs, caches, and containers filled with preps make loading up the car more comfortable.

Conducting a quarterly inventory of your preps will keep your stockpile fresh. Do not forget to include the bugout bags and get home bags in this inventory. Everything should be checked, and any holes should be filled.

Sample Checklist:

- Bottled water
- Food supplies (as a starting point, FEMA recommends enough for 72 hours, but a minimum of a month would be a better idea)
- Way to purify contaminated water
- Camping stove
- Can opener
- Emergency heating (e.g., wood stove - something that does not rely on the grid)
- Emergency candles (also non-grid-reliant - e.g., candles, lanterns)
- Batteries & torches
- Basic tools
- Local maps
- Solar-powered charger

- Battery/solar-powered radio
- First aid supplies
- Hygiene supplies
- Your family's emergency bugout bags
- Reliable transportation (with spare fuel)

KEY CHAPTER CONCEPTS

- Administrative tasks are the first element you should prep.
- Create a home ERP.
- Hard copies of important information should be recorded and kept in one place where everyone can access it.
- Information should be backed up using technology.
- Be sure to include several threats that are unique to your area.
- Run drills to ensure your family is prepared for possible threats.
- Invest in at least one comprehensive hard copy first aid resource.
- Create a detailed evacuation plan and checklist.

3

ESSENTIAL #1 WATER

EVERYTHING YOU NEED TO KNOW ABOUT EMERGENCY WATER STORAGE

M odern preparedness has many parts and pieces, and the scope is growing! This is good news because it makes prepping as rewarding as it is effective. However, just as the First Nations People who built their homes and villages near bodies of water, we understand that water is our number one essential when it comes to prepping.

This can seem crazy because we have a tap that gives us limitless water on demand. It is also very rare that we get a boil water notice and even rarer that the tap water flow is disturbed and our faucets run dry. Because of this, the American people get complacent. You get used to safe drinking water access! It is a marvel of modern society.

However, once that tap runs dry, you have about three days before your internal organs start shutting down due to dehydration. This is what we preppers worry about. Sure the water is everywhere, but when it goes away, the clock starts ticking, and if you do not have an answer, you are either going to flirt with death or have to line up to get rationed water.

To avoid that, you are going to create your emergency water storage solution. While that might sound pretty intense, I can assure you that you will have a bulletproof plan and be ready for water shortages or tap water outages in the future with some simple steps. To achieve this, we are going to focus on four core actions and items.

- Water Storage
- Rain Catchment
- Grey Water
- Water Filtration and Sourcing

Water Storage

One of the easiest steps you can take to prepare for a water crisis is to purchase extra water or water storage containers. If you have the room, you can store a significant amount of water in your home. Of course, you have to know how much water you need. This is simple. You just calculate 3 gallons of water per person per day.

If you know anything about water storage, you might be thinking, 'I thought you only needed 1 gallon of water per person per day?' If we are just talking about hydration, you are right. However, we also have to consider things like cooking, cleaning, and hygiene. In preparing for chaos and disaster, you will store lots of dry food, and that food will require water. If you start pulling from your one gallon of water per person to cook rice and beans, you will either have crunchy beans or thirsty family members.

There are also several places that you are already storing water or could store water in a hurry. One of the most popular storage locations for water is the bathtub. Filling bathtubs is an emergency imperative when preparing for things like hurricanes.

Your water heater and that fire hydrant down the street are both going to be great places that you can source water from your immediate area.

We are talking about 12 gallons of water per day or 360 gallons per month for a family of four.

It is unlikely that you will have the space to store all of that water in your home, but buying gallon jugs and water battles can provide convenient access to safe drinking water in an emergency. You might also consider totes or something like Water Bricks, which are large containers designed for holding water. These can be stacked, and as long as you keep them out of direct sunlight, you can store tap water in them.

Water storage is an important part of your emergency water plan, but realistically it is only one part.

Rain Catchment

The beautiful thing about water is that it falls out of the sky! There is no other resource that is so readily available. The problem is most people do not take advantage of this falling water. They simply watch it wash down their guttering, down the street and into the rainwater drains or through their yards and into the valleys, creeks, and streams that surround their home.

When you think about a number like 360 gallons, it might make you nervous. You can buy 55-gallon rain barrels for around $100 each. There are several varieties. You can also buy 55-gallon, food-safe barrels and make your rain barrels for less than that. Since these barrels hold 55 gallons of water, you can see how quickly those gallons add up after heavy rainfall. With four rain barrels hooked up to your downspouts, you will be able to hold 220 gallons of water just in those four barrels!

The water that drips into your rain barrels is not ready to drink. It will pick up contaminants rolling off your roof and sitting in that rain barrel. You should always filter and boil your water from your rain barrels. This is the best way to keep your family safe. Now, using this water for things like cleaning is much easier and does not require filtering.

Rain catchment is not limited to rain barrels, and you can create any kind of system you like. It is really up to your imagination. You can bury a 1000-gallon cistern in your yard and run a couple of downspouts to it. That would take care of all of your water needs.

You can also catch rainwater off other structures like outbuildings, sheds, chicken coops, and detached garages. When it comes to water, you want to use all of the available resources.

An effective rainwater system can handle a large portion of your emergency water needs.

Grey Water

We waste a lot of water in this nation. We let the hose run, and we take big hot baths. We wash dishes, and that water goes right down the drain and is gone back to the water supply.

However, on homesteads all across this nation, some people collect the water that goes down the drain in a bucket while washing hands or dishes. That water is called greywater and can be used to water gardens, water compost piles, and even complete outdoor cleaning jobs. The amount of water that you can save by using greywater is tremendous.

While catching greywater in buckets can be effective, it can also be a backbreaker! The more efficient homesteaders have created a greywater system that goes directly from the faucet to a cistern or straight into the garden. A simple valve can be used for this purpose. Take a look at your water needs and see if greywater can be something you take advantage of.

Water Filtration and Sanitization

Water collects sediments and pathogens quickly. Most concerning are bacteria and parasites. Giardia and cryptosporidium are two examples of things you want to filter out of your water to make it safe. If these bacteria collect and reproduce in your intestines, it can create serious gastrointestinal illnesses. You will suffer from painful cramps and diarrhea. If water shortage is an issue, then ailments like these will make hydration even harder to achieve.

Every day thousands of people die on our planet because they drink contaminated water. Clean water access is a serious issue, but it is one Americans are far removed from. Water filtration technology has come a long way in the last ten years, and you can now carry a highly effective water filter that filters down to .03 microns or small enough to block things like bacteria and parasites from making it through.

A micron is smaller than anything you can see with the human eye. It is smaller than a white blood cell, red blood cell, and even bacteria. When you filter with a quality water filter, you are using a diameter that is .03 of a micron. We are talking seriously microscopic!

Many filter designs work great and are effective in dealing with bacteria, sediment, and parasites. They might be straw designed, water bottles with contained filters, drip-style filters, or even hand pump style. You can even spend $1000 on a whole house filtration system. Just be sure you stock up on extra filters for your systems.

At the very least, you need a hand pump option. While products like the LifeStraw look great in brochures, you need the ability to refill things like water bottles, bladders, and maybe even pots for cooking. You simply cannot do that with a straw style filter.

The Katadyn Hiker Pro

This filter is what I carry in my bugout bag. It is a powerful hand pump filter that has filtered my water through many an adventure. It is easy to use and lightweight.

HydroBlu Pressurized Jerry Can

This little jerry can filter over 10,000 gallons of water and pump it out into drinking glasses or even a pressurized spray nozzle to wash up or clean. It carries 3 gallons of water and has made a home for itself in our emergency water preparedness plans.

Medium-sized water filtering solutions are essential. No matter which of these technologies you decide on, you need at least one. You could invest in a larger scale water filtering option.

You can also purchase water purification tablets to kill pathogens in your water. Bleach can be used as well; 6-8 drops of unscented bleach per gallon of water can act as a sanitizer for water.

Just remember that any water you catch or source from local streams, no matter how clean it looks, must be filtered, and it should be boiled for 10 minutes too. Remember, the most significant threats in water are too small for the eye to see. You cannot look down into a glass of water and see the pathogens swimming around.

Water Sourcing

Beyond catching and storing water, you also need to know where you can go to source water. I mean springs, wells, or bodies of water that can provide you with a source that will not expire, should be a part of your emergency water plan. From these bodies of water, you can either filter at the water source or you can collect water and process it back home.

Plotting out these water sources can be as simple as printing out an overhead view of your immediate area. Look for streams, creeks, ponds, and rivers in your area. These are all viable water sources. They can be marked on a paper map and visited to get a lay of the land.

The best source of water for drinking is going to come from running water that is deep enough that you can source from just below the surface without picking up sediment from the bottom of the waterbed. The surface of water bodies is contaminated, and most contaminants settle to the bottom. So, you want to pull water from the middle column of the water.

There are things like pollutants that can contaminate bodies of water, and these could be present if you need to move to a different body of water. Know what is upstream from your water source. You want to be careful not to pull water downstream from a business that dumps into the body of water.

Also, pay attention to runoff when you are looking at water bodies and water sources. If you can identify two to three sources for emergency water in your area, you are going to be in good shape if you ever face a water shortage or crisis.

When it comes to emergency water preparedness, you want to focus on options. You want as many options for water as you can muster. The more ways you can source and filter water, the less of a problem you will have staying hydrated in an emergency.

While it might seem like a lot, you can secure your emergency water needs in one weekend! The purchase of some bottles of water, a couple of rain barrels, some mapping of water resources, and the investment in a water filter that will filter down to .03 micron will give you all kinds of options.

Hydration is essential! Water on its own will not replace electrolytes, so you might also want to include some powdered electrolytes that can simply be stirred into the water and used to replace those things you lose when you sweat. It is all around us. It falls from the sky. Do not be caught without safe drinking water for you and your family.

KEY CHAPTER CONCEPTS

- Store some water in the home but not the majority.
- You will need 80-90 gallons of water per person per month.
- Take advantage of rain catchment for the majority of your water storage needs.
- Consider the advantages of capturing and using greywater.
- You need a supply for drinking, cooking, cleaning, and washing.
- Have multiple methods of filtering and sanitizing water in your home.
- Identify at least one large body of water in your area as a potential long-term water source.

4

ESSENTIAL #2 FOOD

PREPARE A PANTRY TO SUPPORT YOUR FAMILIES HEALTH, NO MATTER THE SITUATION

The darkest parts of the 20th century were tied, in some way, to the scarcity of food or resources. The Soviet Famine starved millions of Russians and Ukrainians in the early 20th century. The Great Chinese Famine in the 50s was the deadliest in history and took the lives of some 22 million Chinese people.

Americans live a life of convenience with massive agricultural systems in place to keep supermarket stores full and a steady supply of grain flowing. In 2020 we witnessed what it feels like to go to a supermarket and see empty shelves. We saw shortages in meats, produce, and even dry ingredients.

If you set up a proper food storage plan that features a nutritious pantry, you will not worry about short term food shortages. They won't even phase you! To pull something like this off, you probably think you need thousands of dollars to spend on extra food. You probably think you need to be a master organizer. Neither is true. It is pretty simple.

The reality is that most American households have less than a day's worth of food to sustain the family in an off-grid emergency. In other words, most foods need to be cooked, and you need electricity or fuel to cook these foods. What does that look like in your home? If you factor in real nutrition, how do the ready to eat foods measure up?

Let's look at the four major areas where you can be effective with your emergency food preparedness.

A Prepper's Pantry

The prepper's pantry is designed to be a deep food storage solution for your family. It is important to understand that you are merely adding more of the same food to your cabinets and pantry that you already have on hand when you start building your deep pantry. In other words, if you usually have two cans of pasta sauce in your pantry, your goal should be to expand on that exponentially! This can be done by simply buying one extra can or packet each time you go to the supermarket.

If you buy one extra box of pasta and one extra can of meat sauce each week, you will have 12 easy emergency meals in 3 months. This will add about $3 to your weekly bill depending on where you shop. You can add extra cans of soup, rice, and oats to your weekly purchases too! In no time, you will begin to see the swelling of your pantry. When you have extra food on hand, you will immediately sleep better!

Remember, this expanded pantry should be made up of food items that your family already enjoys. Do not go out and buy food that your family doesn't like just because it has a long shelf life! Your pantry should be filled with weekly meals and snacks. Be sure to include a variety of foods so that you have a balanced diet that maximizes nutrition.

To supplement this pantry diet, you could also beef up your vitamin supply. This should include extra vitamins for adults and children. You might also consider storing protein powder as this can provide your family with essential amino acids if you find meat becomes a scarcity.

Building a robust emergency pantry will not be a financial strain. It will become a test of your focus and commitment. By spending $10 - $20 extra per week, you will begin to see the results in a matter of months, and this is only one aspect of how you address your emergency food storage needs. When SHTF in Suburbia, you and yours will be eating, not having to scramble for food at the store or be forced to eat unhealthy alternatives.

Organization and Rotation

Adding all of this extra food to your home will require you to focus more on the organization of your pantry and the rotation of food. You should always be eating the oldest foods first, and to do this, you need to understand the concept of FIFO (first in, first out). Popularized by the food industry and food safety standards, FIFO is the process of moving out the oldest food first.

FIFO - First In First Out

The simple labeling of shelves can aid this type of organization and rotation. If you know where a specific item goes, it will be easy to understand how much you have. Then it will be easy to pull all of that product forward so you can add the new can, box, or bag behind the oldest food.

If you do not commit to your growing pantry organization and rotation, you will find yourself throwing lots of food out. Lack of organization could also bring pests into your home. Pests will wreak havoc on your food storage and your family's confidence in the food that is stored. If everything has to be inspected for chew marks from a rodent, it will be a big problem.

A simple weekly rotation of foods and occasional cleanout and inspection will keep your food safe, and in an SHTF situation, you will be cooking meals just like you were before the chaos took hold.

Emergency Dried Foods

Some people build up food storage by purchasing freeze-dried meals that come packed safely in containers. These can be stacked and stored anywhere you see fit. They also have a tremendous shelf life. Most of these companies will promise a shelf life of around 20 - 25 years. In the last five years, some of the best emergency food companies have even expanded the variety of foods offered to include things like non-dairy and vegan options. The market is growing, and people are buying these foods every day.

Here is a list of some of the best companies that are selling these foods right now.

- Legacy Foods
- Augason Farms
- Emergency Essentials
- My Patriot Supply
- Wise Food Storage
- Shelf Stable Foods for Long Term Food Storage

DIY Long Term Food Storage

While these companies produce a great product, you too can make your 5-gallon buckets of long-term food storage. It is simple and, thanks to club buyers like Costco and BJ's, you can buy large quantities of discounted food.

Using Mylar bags, oxygen absorbers, and 5-gallon buckets, you can take advantage of discounted food prices and make your own long term food storage.

We store 5-gallon buckets of foods like beans, rice, oatmeal, sugar, and flour. These long-term food storage options are still one of the best investments I have made in my preparedness. It is the kind of nutritional insurance that is ready when disaster strikes.

So how do you do it? Let's look at the simple steps of bucketing up your long-term food storage.

Materials Needed:

- 20-50lbs of dried food (We will use a 50lb bag of rice as an example)
- 5 Gallon Buckets
- 5 Gallon Mylar Bags (These can be purchased online)
- 2000CC Oxygen Absorbers
- Hair Straightener or Iron

Method:

- Set out your 5-gallon buckets and open up your Mylar bags inside the buckets.
- Open your rice and use a clean coffee cup or large scoop with a handle and start filling a mylar bag that is settled into a 5-gallon bucket.

- Fill the Mylar bag about 4/5 of the way, leaving enough of the bag empty so it can be sealed.
- Before sealing, you must drop in an oxygen absorber. This will keep your food safe, dry and kill any bugs packed with the grain.
- Mylar bags can be heat sealed; you can use a hair straightener that is warmed up or an iron to seal these bags.
- Once your bags are sealed, you can place the lids on top, and you have a 5-gallon bucket of long-term food storage!

Stack these in the basement or garage, and you will have some serious food storage in the worst-case scenario. Do not forget to label and date these but be creative. A small label on the bottom might tell you what is in the bucket, and a larger label on the outside might read PRIMER, CEILING PAINT, or something else so that people will never suspect these buckets are filled with food.

Backyard Supermarket

The push to grow food has gripped the nation, and more people are gardening and community gardening than ever before! This inspiration has come from things like the COVID-19 outbreak and its effect on our food supply. Alternatively, the contamination of our food supply with pesticides, and the overall feeling of accomplishment that comes with growing your food, has been used as motivation.

You would be surprised at what you can pull off on a typical urban sprawl with some kind of simple fence to protect from things like deer. Before we had kids, my wife and I spent a brief time living in the suburbs of Virginia. I always loved Virginia. We were on 3/4 of an acre, and I cleared some of it for the man who rented us the property. We used that new space to spike our food production.

In the early days, we had a few raised beds in the backyard and a bunch of potted plants. As we got to know our soil and improved it, we began planting potatoes, squash, and heavy producers like tomatoes, peppers, kale, and cucumbers. We even raised green beans and English peas at varying times of the year.

We had a pretty impressive garden. We grew plenty of potted herbs too. In three years, we had added six laying hens in a small coop, two peach trees, an almond tree, a fig tree, a few different types of perennials, and even grew some shiitake mushrooms in the woods just behind us.

Are you the type of person who looks at the modern homesteaders and yearns for that kind of independence? You are capable of far more than you think!

Growing food takes time, most suburbs are allowing a small amount of laying hens, and no one is going to give you trouble over some fruit trees! Before learning about what you want to grow, you have to understand things like your soil and how to feed plants. You also have to know about the pests and wildlife that will assault your backyard gardens.

While traditional growing and raising animals works well, you could also invest in a hydroponics or aquaponics system that will produce food for you using a water-based growing system. Aquaponics systems will even provide you with fish that are raised right in your backyard!

You have a lot more options than the small garden bed with tomatoes and peppers.

Drying and Canning

If you get your backyard garden and growing systems up and running, you will quickly realize that you cannot eat it all! Even a small tomato garden will have you handing out tomatoes because you will get sick of those things in the high volume that they produce.

Investing in a dehydrator will allow you to dehydrate that backyard harvest. These dehydrated vegetables can be added to your stockpile or mixed with other dehydrated food items that can be combined to create quick meals.

Canning is another great way to take advantage of that backyard harvest. You have the ability to cook down foods, pack fresh, and do all sorts of cool things before canning your foods. Once these food items are safely canned, they can become a part of that growing pantry of yours.

If you get into canning, just be sure that you have a high-quality book or resource you can trust. Canning certain foods will require a pressure canner. Foods that are canned improperly can be dangerous to the health of your family. There is no point in putting up all this food if it is going to cause your family harm.

Preservation has a place in your emergency food plan. Never throw food away again!

THE IMPORTANCE OF SURVIVAL NUTRITION

So much preparation can get muddied by fantasy. While it might be exciting to consider trapping and hunting for food or subsisting off scavenged canned goods without labels and the like. If you want to be at your best, you are going to need to have balanced nutrition.

In an SHTF situation, you are going to be tested more than you ever have been. You are going to be physically and mentally tested, most likely, beyond your limits. You will not be sleeping because of fear and stress, and other routine items will not be happening either. If there is one area that you can positively affect, it is the overall nutrition of your food storage.

Over the last five years, we have seen some incredible studies to suggest that good nutrition and physical fitness can help with battling depression! In an SHTF situation, you better believe there will be some level of depression.

The lack of medications could also exacerbate poor health symptoms, and a good clean diet has been shown to improve things like diabetes. If you can create your emergency food supply from a prepper's pantry, long term food storage, and a garden of fresh fruits and vegetables, you will have a solid base.

While Mountain House is quick and easy, it is not the best form of nutrition. MREs store well, but they are not something you want to eat week over week for every meal. The needs of the human body do not change, even though the surrounding environment does. Keep that in mind while you plan your food storage program.

KEY CHAPTER CONCEPTS

- Emergency food storage begins with a robust pantry filled with the foods you already eat regularly.
- Long-term food storage is designed to give you a safety net and, when appropriately packaged, can last up to 25 years.
- Your backyard or balcony can become a supermarket of its own if you create a viable gardening area.
- Canning and preserving will make your homegrown food supply go even further.
- Do not forget to rotate your food, first in, first out.

5

ESSENTIAL #3 MEDICINE

MAKE SURE YOUR FIRST AID KIT IS BULLETPROOF

We all have bodies, but few of us know how to take care of them. Isn't that crazy? Well, it is not when you think about it. We live in homes we do not know much about, and we drive computerized cars we couldn't fix in a million years!

First aid and medicine are specific skills that have hard limitations. You can learn to do a lot for someone who is injured, but there are things like surgery that you just cannot do unless you are trained. You will likely put the person at more of a risk by trying.

Of course, in an SHTF situation, we are going to be dealing with injury and illness with limited supplies and limited or no access to medical care. That is a serious consideration. When a child is suffering from an injury or illness in bed, and you do not have what you need to help them, everything gets very real.

My travels around the world showed me the austere situations that many people live in across the globe. The human body heals, and it is a marvel, but you should store the right kinds of medical equipment to help it along.

Building a Medical Cache at Home

Most retailers carry "Family" first aid kits. These kits are large and contain a lot of nothing. They are full of items that should be used to restock your first aid cache at home but are not a standalone solution in your home. Of course, having one of these is better than not having anything, but building a medical cache takes more time and thought than a small first aid kit you buy at the store.

Your medical cache will be crafted to meet your needs. You should consider your family members as well. This is the collection of first aid, medical equipment, and medications that you will need to care for your family when you become the doctor! That is a scary thing to consider, but it could quickly become a reality in an SHTF situation. The following list gives you an idea of the types of things you and your family would benefit from having in your first aid cache.

Bandages and Bleeding:

- Medical Tape
- Nitrile Gloves
- Rolled Gauze
- Gauze Pads
- Trauma Shears
- New Skin
- 5 X 9 Abdominal Gauze Pads
- Styptic Powder
- Tourniquets

Ongoing Wound Treatment:

- Splints
- ACE Bandages
- Rubbing Alcohol
- Peroxide
- Triple Antibiotic Ointment
- Aloe Vera
- Essential Oils
- Irrigation

OTC Meds:

- Acetaminophen
- Aspirin
- Anti-Inflammatory Meds
- Anti-Diarrhea

- Cough Suppressant

Prescriptions:

If you are on any type of medication, you need to sit your doctor down and talk to them about how you can get even more of your prescriptions filled. Maybe you can get three months of them in advance.

Of course, the bigger idea is to look at your health, diet, and fitness level and see how you can maximize these. You may just be able to get away from some of these medications with modifications to your diet and exercise.

The Bugout Medical Kit:

We have already established that bugging in or living out an emergency in your home is the best plan A that you can have. However, we wouldn't be preparing for much if we didn't have a plan B. Plan B for most preppers is going to be some kind of bugout. If your home becomes untenable, you will want an option that is your home away from home. You need a place where you can go to outrun the chaos and get back to living.

You will not be carrying your entire medical loadout with you on most bugouts. However, you still need solutions for injuries and illness during the bugout and at the BOL (bugout location).

Carrying medical equipment and first aid on foot is a lot of added weight, and you have to be smart about it. The best method for carrying serious medical preps on a bugout would be to either build or invest in an IFAK (individual first aid kit) for each family member. The IFAK will give you the ability to spread the weight out amongst the group. This is better than having one person weighed down with all the supplies, especially if your group gets broken up.

IFAKs can be purchased and should include bandages, tourniquets, pressure dressing, hemostatic agent to help blood clot, and other lifesaving implements like chest seals. In an IFAK, you should also have simple Band-Aids and ointments to deal with simple wounds, cuts, and scratches.

OTC meds are also great to add to your IFAK. The small packets are the best for this. Be sure to include the things that your family needs. Always have an answer for pain, fever, diarrhea, and congestion.

You could also create a secondary medical cache that could be buried at a location along the way. This means you could carry very minimal first aid along the way and just pick up your medical cache at a particular location when you get closer to the BOL.

Dental Care:

Dental care in SHTF situations is not as complicated as you might think. Now, dental surgery is just that, surgery. So, you should get this stuff handled before any foreseeable chaos hits. Schedule your surgery now if you need it.

Day to day dental care can be handled in several ways. It can be exciting to use survivalists and primitive tactics to care for your teeth and gums. You can just buy a tube of toothpaste every other week at the supermarket and then buy an extra toothbrush once a month. In no time, you will have the basics of dental care in large quantities. Throw some floss in there from time to time, and you will be well set up.

That said, we should also look at several ways that you can naturally affect your dental care in an SHTF situation.

Baking Soda:

This is a great toothpaste when mixed with water. It is simple, cost-effective, and has whitening agents.

Ash:

In Africa, it is very common for tribes to use the ash from their fire to brush their teeth. It might seem primitive, but many cosmetic companies have begun putting activated charcoal in some versions of their toothpaste.

Salt Water:

Simple salt water can do a lot to irrigate and cleanse your mouth. Of course, this assumes you are storing plenty of salt!

Essential Oils:

Essential oils can be added to things like baking soda to create an even better toothpaste.

SHTF dental is not a big issue unless you have a history of bad oral health. Take care of your teeth now! Get into the dentist and get things handled. If it comes down to SHTF dental surgery, just know it is going to hurt. If you know someone who has dental training, you should get to know them a little better!

EDC First Aid:

In an SHTF situation in the suburbs, you might consider carrying first aid wherever you go. I have been carrying a kit of my own for years—a simple kit to deal with things you might need to deal with while you are out.

Carrying things like activated charcoal, Swat Ts, Tourniquets, basic bandages, and some Band-Aids as well as some ointment, sunblock and bug spray, rolled gauze, and tape.

Instruction:

All around the nation, there are tons of classes teaching advanced first aid and trauma care. These courses cost money, but they are hardly the only resource if you do not have the money to go to these classes.

Your community offers a free CERT class at least once a year to help the community learn first aid. This could be a training opportunity for you, and it can be a way to solidify your skills each year and also meet like-minded people.

Books:

There is no substitute for hard copy information when it comes to medical and first aid. There are some books out there that anyone preparing for a medical SHTF situation should have in their library.

LIST OF IMPORTANT MEDICAL BOOKS:

The Survival Medicine Handbook

Dr. Bones and Nurse Amy have been THE voice in the prepping world for SHTF medical care. This was the first book written by Joe Alton M.D, aka Dr. Bones, and touches on everything you need to know about this topic. This is an all-in-one manual.

The Doomsday Book of Medicine

Dr. Ralph Laguardia has put together an incredible book that touches on all aspects of health, wellness, and medical care through the lens of surviving Doomsday. This book goes way beyond simple medical advice and techniques. It also introduces natural remedies and things like using common household ingredients such as baking soda to treat injuries and illnesses.

Alton's Antibiotics

There are some illnesses and injuries that just require antibiotics. You cannot get around it. The average person has no idea what to use and how much of it to use. This book takes care of all of that. It even teaches you how to acquire antibiotics.

Preppers First Aid Handbook

William W. Forgey is a veteran outdoorsman and a full-time practitioner of family medicine. This book is one of the most important. Learn how to deal with things as simple as bites and stings or as wild as building an off-grid medical kit. This book is a must-have for anyone interested in building a medical library for SHTF.

These are examples of great books that should be in your collection. Not to be confused with your first aid manual, these are designed to be for situations that call for more than basic first aid.

KEY CHAPTER CONCEPTS

- Invest your time to create a high-quality first aid kit that is tailored to your needs.
- Make it part of a larger first aid cache full of items you and your family might need in a disaster.
- Outfit cars, backpacks, and vacation homes with quality kits.
- Consider SHTF dental in your medical plans.
- Invest in an SHTF first aid library that can be your reference if you become the family doctor.

6

ESSENTIAL #4 SECURITY

PREPARING TO PROTECT YOUR HOME AND COMMUNITY IN SHTF

Traveling around the world and throughout this nation, I have seen how people live and how safety and security play out differently in different areas. Some communities are guarded by gates, walls, and armed security. I have visited other places on the planet where villages are little more than grass and mud huts with minimal, if any, security.

Throughout history, we have been a people of fortifications and borders. Most nations realized that to remain secure and sovereign, an active military and secure border were essential. Kingdoms of the past went as far as building many walled defenses where attacking forces would have to hurdle several walls to breach the city.

We are living through a time of extraordinary peace in our nation. Sure there are criminals, there will always be criminals, but we are safer now than ever before. Of course, in SHTF, that can all go away, and things can get ugly in a hurry.

You do not need a three-walled defense around your castle, but there are some simple steps you can take to make your home significantly more secure. We are going to discuss the essential security principles in this chapter.

The Importance of Security in SHTF

It is hard for Americans to understand a situation that would be labeled as SHTF. What would the world be like without law enforcement, food, water, and medicine after about two weeks? Can you imagine the chaos in the streets? We have only had glimpses of what this might look like, and it is terrifying. Look back to events like the '92 riots in LA or the events following Hurricane Katrina's fallout.

These glimpses give Americans pause, but few take action to fortify their homes or establish anything beyond a few weeks of vigilance.

To put it simply, the majority of Americans are not prepared for widespread civil unrest. We are untrained and inexperienced. That is a testament to our society and the relative peace we have seen in recent decades.

I need you to understand that you and those around you will become the security detail in an SHTF situation. All the layers of protection, from the police to alarm systems, will dissolve, and no one will be coming to help you. That is the level of importance of this chapter.

The 3 D's of Home Defense

Thanks to our innovative military, there is a system in place that makes almost every aspect of emergency preparedness easier. When it comes to security and defense, there is one system that is easy for anyone to understand and to act on.

These are the 3 D's of Home Defense and Security:

- Detect
- Deter
- Defend

Using these three principles, you will be able to take actionable steps on any threat to your community or home. Once you have a plan, everything gets a lot less nerve-racking.

Detect

The detection of a threat is the first step in this system. This identifies a problem, a person, a group, or something else that just does not fit. There are two degrees of detection. The simple version is peeking out the blinds and seeing someone walking the streets late at night that you do not recognize. My mother was a champion at this method! She was always in those blinds. You could also be actively detecting threats by using things like cameras, trail cameras, or even drones to monitor your property.

You can look at detection from the standpoint of a home-owner. How best can you detect threats from your home? However, detection truly works best at the community level. A community threat detection system can be as simple as a communications network like the Nextdoor App and a few vigilante neighbors. As long as you can detect and report, you have a powerful system in your community.

Here are Some Great Tools for Detecting Threats in and Around Your Home:

- Optics (binoculars, monocular, night vision)
- Security Cameras on the Home
- Trail Camera
- Other Community Members
- Late Night and Early Morning Walks
- Perimeter Alarms

Detection is step one to understanding the nature of the threat you face. It could be an immediate threat, or it could be someone scoping your home or community out. Without detection, you could be unaware, and then it might be too late to react. There is a reason that we place defend at the end of this system. Detecting and deterring can be very careful.

If you decide to neglect these, it will also be awfully hard to be in the most advantageous position. Through detection and deterrents, you can identify a threat and give yourself ample time to consider the best way of dealing with that threat.

Deter

When you think about an SHTF scenario in suburbia, you go right to the AR15 and an ample supply of ammo. You invent a terrifying threat in your head, and then you consider the quickest way to mitigate that threat, whether that be a bunch of guys at your doorstep or a single intruder breaking in to steal food or to hurt your family.

It is quite common for preppers to get engrossed in firearms. Firearms can be a solution to a very severe problem, but the truth is, there are several ways that you can deal with threats to you and your property. The strategic prepper will spend most of their time on deterrents when it comes to home security.

Deterrents are practical and straightforward, and they can go a long way when it comes to avoiding severe security threats. With the overreliance on firearms, it is easy to forget that when you start firing rounds at a person, they could begin to fire rounds back!

Better than any tricked-out rifle is the ability to force the mind of a criminal to look away from your home without taking any action yourself. This comes from careful and strategic deterrents that have a psychological effect on the people casing your house.

This might all sound way too complicated. Maybe you are not a strategic person, but you like the idea of avoiding a firefight and setting your home up in such a way that the bad guys avoid it. To simplify all this talk of strategy, I am going to give you one sentence to consider.

Your home should be less desirable than the other houses on your block!

It comes down to desirability. Take a look at the homes around yours. Focus on them. Maybe take a walk and look at the yards, fences, and entrances to the houses. Then you need to start thinking like a criminal.

- Which house would be the easiest to break into?
- Which house could you break into without being seen by others?
- Which house provides the best way out without being seen?

These are all the types of things that criminals consider when they are casing a property. If they see a home that has no cars in the driveway and is empty most of the day, well, there is potential there. You can rely on the sad reality that most Americans take ZERO precautions when attempting to deter criminals.

This means that every step you take to set up deterrents is going to put your home lower and lower on the list of desirable properties in your neighborhood for criminals. It will be tiny tweaks here and there that make your home safer. You could argue that building giant walls around the home might be too much of a deterrent.

It is possible to fortify your home overly. The right number of deterrents puts criminals off, but a serious obstacle piques their interest and makes them wonder, *what are they protecting in there?* The perception might be something valuable is hiding behind those bars and walls.

Dogs

These little creatures have been the human alarm system for thousands of years. They are the best. Though I have snuck up on my dogs in the dark of night while they were sleeping, if someone starts banging at your door at night, you will know it. Dogs give you a heads up, but they also just deter. If a criminal has a choice between the quite empty home and the home with a dog, it is a no brainer!

Security System

A quality security system can act as a deterrent. Good criminals will know how to work around it, but you should broadcast it if you have a good system, so the bad guys know.

Secure Windows

The easier it is to get in, the more likely people will get in. If a bad guy has to rattle and wrench at the windows, they run the risk of being seen or waking up the homeowner.

Good Lighting

Motion lights and floodlights are great ways to keep your doors visible. High visibility at the front and back doors makes criminals nervous. They do not want to be seen coming or going. Bright lights will keep them from picking your home.

Gates

If they can walk right up to your home without hopping fences or opening gates, that's a good day for a criminal. A gate is another level of deterrent.

Clear and Open Yards

Yards that are filled with bushes, trees, and junk will provide a criminal with all kinds of options. The more hiding spots they have on the way to your side window or backdoor, the more likely they are to target your home.

Cars in Driveway

Does someone work from home? If there is a car in the drive and someone milling about at all times, then criminals are just going to keep on walking by. The last thing most criminals want is any interaction with the human element. Even if you take 2-3 of these deterrents and focus on them, you will make your home more of a sanctuary. You will have a home that is completely unappealing to society's worst elements, and that is precisely where you want to be.

Fortifying Your Home

When it comes to fortifying the home, you can wade into the realm of fantasy if you aren't careful. You could find yourself trying to turn your home into a bunker from which you can fight a war. That is the wrong train of thought. If you do not believe me, I want you to answer one simple question.

Who in Your Home is an Acceptable Casualty?

In military operations, there is a metric known as acceptable casualties. It is expected that there will be casualties in a military engagement. Suppose there aren't any on that particular mission, well, great! However, they plan on losing people on certain missions. When you start looking at yourself as more of a soldier than a spouse and parent, that is a problem.

The answer to the question is that your family unit is not prepared to lose anyone. Therefore, you cannot operate as a force that is prepared to take and return gunfire. If you are pretending like that is an option, then you are insane. For this reason, above all, you should not plan on fortifying your home for war. We will talk about what the better option is in the next section.

If you are dead set on fortification, I would say that improving doors and windows can go a long way. Most doors are weak. Locks are easy to bypass, and hinges can be removed with a good crowbar. A strong metal door can go a long way, and a company called Door Armor will help you fortify all the susceptible areas on your doors.

You can replace locks on windows and replace old windows. You can even install bulletproof glass on your windows too! This means that a typical smash-and-grab gets a lot harder for the average criminal.

Think of fortification as less about shooting the AR15 from behind sandbags and more about breaking the will of people who want to get into your home. This sounds complex and arduous, but to be honest, most people aren't that strong-willed. Criminals are professional opportunists, and the opportunity is fleeting. The right moment to take a home comes and goes quickly.

If your locks are fortified and your windows do not break, you will not only be alerted, but the criminals will also run off because they realize the operation has been compromised. Focus on breaking the will of the criminal from afar.

THE IMPORTANCE OF ESTABLISHING A DEFENSIVE PERIMETER

In an SHTF situation, the basic criminal will not be your only threat. Threats will be more common, and attacks will be more severe. So, you should go above and beyond the idea of home security. Home security is designed to address threats that can be handled at the household level. SHTF is not a situation that should be handled by a single household. SHTF is a community or a neighborhood problem.

The scope of your security expands, and you find yourself trying to understand how not just to keep your home safe but how do you keep a whole neighborhood safe. The great news is the same principles apply. You can detect, deter, and defend a community by using a simple defensive perimeter.

Creating your Community Boundary

To execute a community-wide defensive perimeter, you first have to define the boundary. It is up to you, in most cases, to determine the borders of your neighborhood. You need a reliable map of your community to start this process. This map will give you all the clues you need to define the perimeter in your neighborhood.

Some easy identifiers can help you establish that perimeter. Let's look at some of those identifiers.

Main Roads

Main roads need to be cut off. You need to set up a perimeter off the main roads. There is too much trouble that can occur there.

Access

Access to your perimeter is essential. People need to be able to easily walk that perimeter and identify and eliminate threats quickly and effectively.

Ability to Defend

These areas should also be easy to defend. You should have cover and high ground all along your perimeter. You will need a topographic map for this.

Vantage Points

Vantage points are designed to give those who are monitoring the perimeter a means of using optics or their eyes to see threats coming from a long way away. This is the most crucial part because you do not want to meet a threat with one person. You want to meet a threat with a force that deters them first.

Once you have established this defensive perimeter, you need to calculate how many patrolled positions are necessary to make this perimeter effective. You also need to know how many people are required to operate each position.

A perimeter position is not one person per position. Instead, it is more like one position equals four people. These people have to go home. Eventually, they have to eat and use the bathroom. So, you need multiple people to man each position. If you have five defensive positions along your perimeter, that could mean that you need 20 people in total to man those positions! That's a lot of people!

As this endeavor will require so many people, a level of democracy will have to go into your plans. You can be the architect of the perimeter and maybe even have some gear that can be handed out amongst people in your group. However, you are going to have a lot of nuances to discuss with 20 people who are working a defensive perimeter in your community. So, leave some things open for interpretation.

Define the perimeter, establish a communications method, and ensure that everyone understands the importance of this. From there, your community must have their say. You might hate it, but you need to hear them out.

Do Not Fight a War From Your Porch

Imagine the world has been turned completely upside down, and there is chaos in the streets. Imagine that there was no plan to get things back under control, and you and yours are huddled in your home, hoping to avoid the chaos. Maybe you have taken the steps we mentioned in previous chapters, and you were somewhat prepared.

In the dark of night, you are woken by a rumble outside of your home. You hop up out of bed. Your head is foggy, and you are quickly trying to wake up. Out the window, you see so many lights. When you part the blinds of your bedroom window, you see four pickup trucks lined up outside of your home, and there are multiple men, armed men, hopping out of the trucks and spreading out through your community.

What do You do Next?

If you find yourself in a situation like this, your security protocols have failed drastically. You cannot fight a war from your porch because you have everything to lose, and the men on the trucks can just go wild. You put your family at risk, you put your community at risk, and your preps, too! These guys are here for what you have. That could be food, ammo, or even people!

Your greatest motivation in neighborhood security is to ensure this never happens. Even if it requires that you create checkpoints and barriers to get into your neighborhood, it is well worth it. Even if you drop trees and park cars to assure that driving into your community is impossible, that is what must be done to avoid fighting a battle from your porch.

Once the bad guys are inside your community, you are going to lose a lot of people. You will have to retreat or create a new formation using radios while you are under attack. Unless you practice this in your community through drills, it is highly unlikely that it will ever happen. It is more likely the bad guys will move through your community, take everything, and kill the people.

This is the importance of security. This is the reason you need firearms and plans to ensure you stop threats at the perimeter of your community. This one scenario is why you live by the three Ds of security.

A NOTE ON FIREARMS

It is easy to go deep and get side-tracked on the path of developing your prepper arsenal. For some, this is most of the fun. You will need firearms if you are going to survive an actual SHTF situation in the suburbs. There is no getting around this part of the game. If the police are gone, and the bad guys have guns, you only have one option.

Let me save you a bunch of time and some arguments by giving you the very best loadout for new preppers and maybe all preppers. You might expect to see something like an AR15 or an AK47 on my list. However, those guns do not even make the top 3. You can accomplish everything you need to, from security to food procurement with three guns. These three guns are going to make your life much easier and will be weapons you use regularly. These firearms have been my go-to for many reasons.

- Ease of use
- Plentiful Ammo
- Affordable
- Effective

9MM Semi-Automatic Handgun

9mm ammunition is some of the most highly distributed in the nation. The gun itself has plenty of stopping power, and most have a minimal kick for a new shooter. These guns can be had for under $300.

The 9mm is also a great weapon to be carried daily. Having a firearm on your person each day is the best way to ensure your safety. As society degrades and violence becomes more prevalent in our streets, you will want a cheap and effective weapon at your side, just in case.

12 Gauge Shotgun

You can put a different sized shot through your 12 gauge, and all will be devastating to your prey. This is a great hunting weapon and maybe the best home defense weapon on the market.

Ammo for your 12 gauge is cheap and easy to get. A cheap shotgun is only going to run you about $200 bucks.

.117 Pump Air Rifle

You could argue about having a powerful hunting rifle, or you could talk about having a .22 rifle over an air rifle.

The air rifle is such an excellent option for preppers because you can use it for hunting small game, you can kill varmints and animals that are eating up your garden. If you buy the right model, this gun can even deter people because they look pretty similar to real rifles to the untrained eye.

However, the big win with the air rifle comes through ammo. Even though a .22 long rifle is cheap ammo, you cannot beat a 500 count for under $20. These guns are also very affordable, and most are around $100 for a good model.

KEY CHAPTER CONCEPTS

- Understand the 3 D's of security.
- Focus your efforts on deterrents.
- Establish a community perimeter.
- Do not plan on fighting a war from your front porch.
- Consider the right firearms for you and your family.

7

ESSENTIAL #5 ENERGY

ARE YOU READY TO SURVIVE OFF-GRID?

Our reliance on things like clean running water and limitless electricity has made American life an absolute dream. It is a dream we often take for granted until one of these services is shut off. When the power goes out, most people are so angry that their electricity party has come to an end.

We are mostly incapable of sitting quietly and enjoying the power loss. For most of us, these outages last hours at the most.

Have you ever contemplated what life might be like if the electricity went off and never came back on? Are you prepared for that? You might not even realize it, but electricity is responsible for so many things.

- Electric Stoves
- Fridges
- Hospitals
- Communications
- Pumping Gas
- Heating
- Air Conditioning
- Entertainment
- Cell Phones

Grid Down Causes

So, how on earth could we find ourselves in this situation? What would it take to bring down the grid forever?

Unfortunately, it is not as complicated as you might assume. The American power grid is mostly unprotected, hard to repair, and susceptible to several attacks and even natural threats.

Electromagnetic Pulse (EMP)

Since the nuclear detonation near Bikini Island, we understand an EMP's potential to do serious damage to an electrical grid. The power of atomic bombs in the 40s was much different than today.

How Different?

The Fat Man that was dropped on Japan was a 21-kiloton bomb. The Castle Bravo, which our most powerful known modern nuclear weapon, is a 15-megaton bomb.

The output difference is massive, and the results are terrifying. The fallout is far more expansive, and a weapon of this size could trigger an enormous EMP.

A high-altitude detonation over the central US would create an EMP capable of crippling our three main power grids. This would effectively send us back to the 1800s.

However, humankind is not the only threat when it comes to an EMP. Our life-giving sun has more than enough power to put the lights out on us with just a single burp of plasma. You see, the sun releases solar flares that occur when the sun's magnetic field is disrupted. The lines twist and snap, releasing a massive flare.

If a solar flare of the right size were to hit the planet, it would cause a worldwide blackout. One of the right size passed through our orbit, but we weren't at that point in our revolution. Many believe it is only a matter of time.

Terrorism

One of the best ways for a terrorist group to stop the United States in their tracks would be to launch a coordinated attack on one or more of the nation's major electrical grids. These three grids are massive and hard to repair and replace.

Most of the components come from China, so if we were to find ourselves at odds with that nation, we could have real trouble.

Human Resources

Every day some men and women go to work with the sole purpose of keeping your lights on. That is an astounding thing when you think about it.

If we were to face an event that disrupted their ability to go to work and operate the power stations, there could be no power without the people who make it possible each day. This type of event could be a pandemic that makes too many workers sick, or it could come from civil unrest that locks people in their homes to avoid violence. If human resources are affected, then our electricity will be shut off.

Backup Power Options

Just because the power grid goes down does not necessarily mean you and yours must be out of power. Thanks to the motivation to fuel our planet with cleaner energies, we have been exploring many backup power options or even off-grid power.

There are plenty of people in this nation who live strictly off-grid and are not even tethered to the power grid or the water system. If you aren't planning on moving to an off-grid homestead anytime soon, you can still affect your response to short- and long-term power outages.

Portable Gas Generators

The portable gas generator is probably the most afford-able and most effective means of powering up the home during an outage. Portable gas generators can be small systems that you can carry or larger systems on wheels.

For years, we have depended on a 5500-watt system in power outages. These give us the ability to turn on lights, television, and entertainment, keep the fridge going, and even power some fans in the summer. It is more than enough power to get through a short-term power outage.

The problem with a reliance on gasoline is that we are only capable of storing so much. This means you will eventually run out of gas in a long-term scenario.

Whole House Generators

The next level of generating electricity is a whole house generator that is often tapped into a natural gas flow. These generators are built into your home and will click on when the power goes out. People love these larger generators because they just keep normalcy rolling even when others are out of power.

The whole house generator is a serious investment and can cost tens of thousands of dollars to install.

In an SHTF situation, the whole house generator could make you a target if you have all your lights on and HVAC (heating, ventilation, and air conditioning) running while the collapsing world around you is struggling.

Solar Panels

Solar power is a very interesting backup power solution. Harnessing the power of the sun just makes good sense. Solar panels can be pieced together over time, or you can go with a professional company to outfit your home.

The solar panels themselves are not affected by an electromagnetic pulse. However, some of the components will be. Safely storing backup components will give you the ability to generate power even after an EMP.

Solar panels cost roughly $1 per watt of energy generated, and DIY is not as hard as you might think. The most critical consideration in all of this is to ensure you get enough sun to power the batteries in your system day after day.

Wind Power

Wind power is another option when it comes to backup power. However, a wind power system can only really generate power if you have plenty of fans and space, like a wind farm, or if you live in a place that is essentially windy all the time.

The wind pushes the rotating blades, and the electricity generated is stored in batteries. The trouble comes when the wind dies down. A wind power system is ineffective if you do not have consistent wind to blow those turbines or turbines high up enough to capture the wind above you.

SHORT TERM POWER OUTAGE PREPAREDNESS

(Up to one month with the expectation that power is coming back on)

In a short-term power outage, you are going to have issues, but they will be nothing like a long-term power outage. Still, you will want to have several plans and things in place to deal with the surprise short-term power outage.

Simple Tip:

Outdoor solar lights are a great option for home lighting during a power outage. The solar lights that sit in your driveway or on your fence posts can be brought inside to light your home in the short term. They are very useful for this purpose and save your candles and flashlight batteries.

Step 1: Blackout Kit

The blackout kit is a fundamental prep that all homes should have on hand. This is an immediate response kit that allows you to get lights into people's hands and get started determining why you are in the dark.

This kit sounds cool, but creating one can be very simple. You do not need a whole lot of high-tech equipment. Our blackout kit consists of:

- flashlights
- lanterns
- candles
- power banks
- emergency radio

With these items, we can light up the night, the home and also get information on weather in the area and other news about what might have caused the power outage if it wasn't weather-related.

Flashlights for the whole family, especially for small children, are particularly important to have in the blackout kit. This way, no one is afraid of the situation.

Step 2: Initiate Potential Backup Power Systems

Now that everyone has a means of lighting up their immediate area, you can start taking the next steps. One of the first things to consider is what you will do with backup power. This depends on the type of power outage you are experiencing. If you call your power company and they tell you that power will be back on in an hour or two, then you probably aren't going to drag out the generator.

However, if you have hours or days even, you might look to start up that backup power system.

Step 3: Charge

If you connect to a backup power option, you should initially consider any items that will be needed for the power outage duration. Ideally, the items you have on hand are already charged so that you will have some time, but you should make sure all things are charged up when you are running backup power. You could also use the power banks from your blackout kit to charge up items.

Step 4: Conserve

Backup power is what it is, and it should be conserved at all costs. If you are working off a solar battery, you want to be careful with how much power you drain off that battery.

Be sure that only the essentials are running and turn everything off when it is not in use. Things like fans and simple lights are easy to forget. If the power outage happens at night, you can fall asleep and leave them on overnight. Conservation can be hard with kids because they will want everything back to normal. Practicing having the power off for a few hours every couple of months will help them have a working experience if and when the real power outage occurs.

Step 5: Wait

With any short-term power outage, there is going to be time. You are going to have some time to chill out and play games or just connect as a family. These things are important. We rarely get time to play a board game or just talk without phones, television, and other interruptions.

You could also go out and eat or just enjoy the outdoors while you wait for the power to come back on. Looking up at the stars when the town has no lights on is a great way to bond with your children and family.

LONG TERM POWER OUTAGE PREPAREDNESS

(Anything over one month without assurance that power will return)

A long-term power outage is chaos. There is no getting around it. We have never witnessed a peaceful long-term power outage in a populated area. It just does not happen. These two things are night and day.

The reality is, most people are not prepared to deal with a long-term power outage. They do not have the food, fuel, or even extra money stored up to pay bills and take care of day-to-day life. For a long-term power outage, you need to look at the situation much differently than being out of power for a week.

When I say long-term, I am talking about a situation in which the power will be out for a month or more! Maybe the power will never come back on again, and we talked about how that could happen at the beginning of the chapter. In a situation like this, you have to make hard decisions. The first and most important of which is whether you are going to stick this power outage out at home or if you are going to evacuate or even bug out until the power returns.

Planning to bug in or stay home during a long-term power outage makes a lot of sense because you will have all of your preps on hand. You will have neighbors around you, and you will be close to family.

By leaving for a bugout location, you are cutting yourself off from some of these benefits. However, you might also be getting away from any serious threats. If you are in a big crowded city, then you need to get away from that place in a long-term power outage. There are just not enough resources to sustain everyone, and things will get ugly in a hurry.

Most of us will choose to bug in and face this grid-down scenario with the preps that we have stored at home and the skills we have developed. Make no mistake about it. The grid-down scenario is among the most dangerous of all disasters.

There will be many things for you to address, and this means that an off-grid emergency deserves a written emergency response plan. Do not try to juggle all the different changes and needs on instinct. You are preparing, right? To best execute, you should have a full-scale off-grid plan.

This plan should start by gathering the family at your chosen location. No matter what time of the day or night it is, you need to get everyone home or to a secure site. The best way to draw this plan up is to create your plan for the middle of a workday. If you are at work, your kids are at school, and your spouse is at work, how do you get home and get everyone to safety.

It all starts with having a location for everyone to meetup. Remember, most grid-down situations are going to affect your ability to communicate drastically. Cell phones will either not work, or networks will be entirely blocked as the mass of people panic and begin to understand what is happening.

Your plan to rally the family at a disclosed location will need to happen with or without communications. This is not that big of a hurdle if everyone in your family understands where they will meet.

If you have young children, the best place to meet is going to be at their school. If you have one young child and one older but not old enough to walk to your younger child's school, parents should know exactly which child to pick up and go right home. This is a simple process, but if you are confused, or you do not have a plan, then it will make things much worse.

From the moment your family is gathered together, your plan becomes very personal. I cannot tell you how to build out your off-grid preparedness plan. All I can say is that all of your preps will help you survive a grid down scenario much better than leaving them behind for another location. If you can stay home and weather the storm, do that!

Essential Items in a Power Outage

There are many items that you will need to consider in a power outage. Things like hygiene, food preparation, security, and sanitation are some of the biggest ones. Let's look at a list of essentials for which you will likely need to find alternatives.

Alternative Lighting:

- Blackout Kit
- Candles
- Rechargeable Solar Lights
- Flashlights
- Headlamps
- Oil Lamps
- Natural Lighting
- Changing your sleep patterns (go to bed when the sun goes down)

Alternative Cooking:

Most stoves are electric, so you need a plan for off-grid cooking. The following are a list of many alternatives to electric cooking:

- Propane Camping Stoves
- Wood Burning Stove
- Outdoor Grills
- Outdoor Wood Fired Pizza Oven
- Alcohol Stove
- Rocket Stove
- Butane
- Propane
- Pressure Cookers (Fuel Conservation)
- Solar Ovens

Alternative Heating:

- Wood Burning Heaters
- Electric Space Heaters
- Fireplace
- Propane Heater
- Alcohol Heater

Is it a Long Term or Short-Term Power Outage?

One of the most important parts of energy preparedness is your ability to discern between a short-term power outage and a full-scale EMP attack. As you can tell, these two are very different. The short-term power outage is something we all efficiently manage regularly, while the EMP is a world-changing event that will lead to many people's death.

Obviously, the quicker you can discern between the two, the faster you will react, and the more effective you will be. The good news is that you can take some quite simple steps to tell whether or not you are experiencing an EMP. Because of the drastic effect it has on our power grid. You can tell in just a few minutes if you know what you are looking for.

Step 1: Check your lights and breakers. Ensure the power to your home is completely out.

Step 2: Check your vehicle. All modern vehicles are controlled through computers and electronics. These will be disabled following an EMP. Unless you have an old car, your car will be inoperable.

Step 3: Check your phone. Your phone will also be dead following an EMP.

Step 4: To avoid a potentially embarrassing reaction, check with your neighbor. If they are suffering from the same situation with phone, power, and car. You are facing an EMP.

Step 5: Check the skyline, highways, or distant lights at night. The EMP causes massive power surges, and these power surges will cause fires. You should see no lights but the distant glow of a fire.

If you are facing an EMP, you have to understand that it will be one of the toughest survival challenges to face.

This is the very worst-case scenario when it comes to emergency preparedness.

Creating a simple blackout kit will help you deal with the majority of blackouts that you and your family face. You should also consider some alternative power sources for longer-term blackouts that follow things like hurricanes and other natural disasters.

If you are genuinely interested in beating the power outage, then you should be on a mission to slowly and thoughtfully remove yourself from the power grid. You might be able to achieve this solely through solar power. It might take a combination of renewable energies to pull this off and a change of your lifestyle.

No matter your approach to dealing with energy preparedness, you will need to collect stored alternatives for cooking, light, electricity, a blackout kit, and a long-term power outage plan. Be sure you can gather the family in a no comms grid-down scenario, and you will be starting in the right place.

KEY CHAPTER CONCEPTS

- There are many ways that we can lose power – some short-term, some long-term.
- Consider the solar and backup gas-powered generators as ways of turning the power back on.

- Be prepared with some off-grid, no electricity preps to help you cook, clean, and have fun in a power outage.

8

ESSENTIAL #6 HYGIENE

ARE YOU READY TO STAY CLEAN AND DEAL WITH YOUR FAMILY'S WASTE?

What is the number one killer in SHTF? Do you fear the biker gangs or the gang leaders or the bands of desperate roving people? Thanks to Hollywood and works of fiction, we assume the human threat is the greatest in SHTF. We prepare because we do not want our lives to end at the wrong end of a knife or a gun barrel.

In reality, you are far more likely to be taken out by an infection or illness. Thanks to modern medicine and easy access to clean water, we rarely concern ourselves with infection. If you do away with waste management and good personal hygiene, suddenly, those old concerns our ancestors had can come roaring back. Just by losing access to clean water, you start a chain reaction of all kinds of problems.

You and yours will need an inventory of personal hygiene items. You will also need the means to deal with your waste and likely agree with neighbors that they will do the same with their waste, or else all your work will be in vain.

If trash is allowed to pile up all over your town or community, remember trash collectors will not be coming each week during SHTF, you will eventually have trash all over the streets, and next will come disease-causing pests. Now you have to worry about dealing with diseases and other issues that go along with pests. One of the big ones is how they get into your home and break into your food storage or pantry.

THE 6 KEY AREAS TO SANITATION

Personal Sanitation

We have come a long way in terms of personal hygiene. Did you know there was a time, not that long ago, when humans fought the scourge of fleas and lice? Not fleas on their dogs but on themselves. It was so bad that people in medieval times chose to lay their clothes over the privy chamber or toilet so that the fumes would delouse and de-flea their clothing!

Modern bathing practices and daily hygiene have made this a non-issue for most people in America. However, we rely on a consistent stream of clean water and access to several resources that keep us clean and free from infection. If you are going to build a cache of personal sanitization items, you are going to want to keep a few things on hand at all times.

- Single-Use Hygiene Items
- Essential Oils
- Waste Collection

Baby wipes, nitrile gloves, toilet paper, and trash bags are all going to be essential when it comes to storing single-use items. You could also include hand sanitizer.

Essential oils are a great ally in any personal hygiene program. Many people will store up toothpaste and deodorant as part of their hygiene preps. However, if these items were to become scarce, you can do a lot of things with essential oils, baking soda, and salt.

Simple Toothpaste

Materials:

- 1/2 Cup of Baking Soda
- 10 Drops of Mint Essential Oil
- 1 TSP of Salt

Method:

The method is quite simple for making this. All you do is mix the ingredients. You can add more or less mint depending on your personal preferences.

Simple Deodorant

Materials:

- 4 TBSP of Arrowroot
- 1 TBSP of Baking Soda
- 10 Drops of Lavender Oil

Method:

These items can be mixed and used under your arms, or you can add a half cup of witch hazel and use this as a spray-on.

As you can see, there are some aspects of personal hygiene preparedness that can be made and not bought. It is better to have the skills to make these items rather than just rely on someone else to make them, and you have access to them. There could come a time where the toothpaste isn't available anymore.

When it comes to building your cache of single-use items, there is one method that works best. Simply buy yourself a large bin, trash can, or some other large lidded container. Whenever you are out shopping, buy yourself an extra pack of toilet paper, a bar of soap, or some sanitary wipes. Just start piling these into that one large bin, and over six months, you will be packed, deep, with soap, toilet paper, and other single-use hygiene items.

Showering and Bathing

In many ways, we can turn back to the water section when it comes to showering and bathing. The water catchment becomes particularly important to personal hygiene. This is another reason why I recommend storing 3 gallons of water per person per day rather than just 1 gallon.

Not only will you want to have access to that water, but you may even want to invest in some sort of backup shower system. If you have plumbing knowledge, you could pipe water into your existing shower pipes.

If you aren't into that, you should invest in a simple camping shower system. They sell a bunch of these of differing varieties. A simple camping shower can feel amazing if you have not had a full-body wash in several days. There is no getting around the fact that you need to clean your body from time to time.

Between showers, you might also look to wipe yourself down for a more straightforward cleaning solution. There is a company called Combat One that makes incredible wipes that contain antibacterial colloidal silver. These wipes can be used to clean your entire body. Having some kind of wipe in an SHTF situation will be very important to cleanliness.

Bathing will likely dominate, and a shower will be a rare occurrence. Bathing in SHTF means transporting large amounts of water from your water reserves to your bathtub. Be sure you have some large pots or totes to pull that off.

Human Waste Disposal

Human waste disposal is something we have been doing since the Romans! While it was hardly as polished as our systems today, it was well understood that we could not live amongst our filth. When the water stops running or the toilets back up, do you have a game plan for dealing with human waste?

If your game plan is to dig catholes, or 6-inch-deep holes in the ground, to manage waste, I would encourage you to expand on that thought. While catholes can be useful on camping trips and missions, the area around your home should not be riddled with cat holes and human waste. You also have to consider the winter and how digging holes and using the bathroom out in the open will work. It won't!

The good news is there are many alternatives when it comes to dealing with human waste disposal. When it comes to these kinds of challenges, I always look to the communities of people who already live off-grid and are doing these things daily.

What would be perfect is if you could turn your waste into food for your gardens and plants? Well, that is precisely what some off-grid homesteaders do using composting toilets. These small toilets are used in the process of making something dubbed "humanure." While our feces are not safe like goat or horse, they can be made so. It has to go through its composting process.

Compost toilets have a small crank handle that is turned after each use to start this process. You can have a larger sawdust and waste system outside the home that turns the waste into something usable.

You could also dig and build an outhouse. These can be highly effective and shelter you while using the bathroom. The digging in your area should be done with the local restrictions in mind. There are lots of rules about how deep and how far away from water they should be. Beyond the hole, the outhouse is a simple build to encase the person using it and allow for ventilation.

Another very simple setup is to use a simple bucket with a fashioned toilet seat. You can start by layering peat and sawdust at the bottom of the 5-gallon bucket. Between uses, you cover the waste completely with peat and sawdust. When full, this mix will go to a larger pile outside, which could be turned into humanure.

Simple Handwashing Station

Human feces are very dangerous. Do you know that our intestinal tract is full of bacteria like salmonella, E. Coli, viruses, and other pathogens? If allowed to hang around, these bacteria will grow and become extremely dangerous to the people exposed to them. This exposure will happen when you use toilet paper. To mitigate the risks, we need to be prepared to set up a simple hand washing station.

Here are the Items You Will Need to Set up Your Simple Handwashing Station:

- Liquid Soap
- Water Source (Raised rain barrel can be great for this)
- Single-Use Paper Towels
- Hand Sanitizer
- Trash Can

If you can manage human waste and clean your hands and arms when dealing with that waste, you will keep disease and infection at bay. This is a fundamental concept because we do not consider it, but we will all have to consider it in an SHTF situation.

Without proper human waste management, we will cont-aminate the local water resource and bring pests and disease into our living areas.

Solid Waste Disposal

Solid waste disposal is probably the most underappreciated service in the world. This is something that happens every week to keep our streets and waterways clean. Most Americans have no idea how much waste they produce. A family of 4 produces roughly a full trash bag of waste each day, from packaging to food waste, to cleaning waste.

Our waste is not only collected from our homes, but it is taken far away and stored in a variety of ways to keep it out of our view. It is a weird system because we bury most of our trash, and some we just throw in lots outside of town.

If not for the weekly trash collection, our streets would be piled high with solid waste. We are a packaged society. With the influx of online shopping, we are disposing of even more packaging at the residential level.

You need to have a plan to deal with solid waste in a suburban SHTF situation, and your plan better include others. The suburbs are very different from living in the country. In the country, you can manage your trash the way you like and not have to worry about your neighbor a mile down the road.

However, in the suburbs, your neighbors' trash will be your trash in a hurry. All that goes along with your neighbor's trash will also be yours. Trash piles will bring pests, it will blow into your yard, and eventually, you will have a severe health hazard in your community.

Lifestyle Changes for Managing Solid Waste

You can limit your waste both in your home and in your community by changing your lifestyle and how you manage solid waste. You can save all kinds of space in your garbage bags when you start composting food waste. We waste a lot of food and parts of food. Rinds, moldy bread, and out of date produce make up a large portion of waste. This stuff can be turned into plant food! Do not miss out on this.

Plastic and glass containers can go a long way. We often throw those glass containers away or put them in recycling. You can also just turn those pickle jars into drinking glasses! You can store nuts and bolts in them or whatever else. These are great little containers. Hard plastic containers can be reused as well. Remember, your ability to reuse things in an SHTF situation will benefit you and your family!

Packaging that cannot be reused needs to be broken down, so it takes up the least amount of space possible. Breaking down packaging gives you the ability to fit more into a smaller area. Crushing things like cans and breaking down cardboard and plastic containers goes a long way. However, you will eventually have to do something with this garbage. You are likely going to have to burn some of your garbage on a weekly basis. This is where you might consider a community setup rather than a personal one. If you have a place where neighbors can lug their trash and burn it, you will likely have less of a pile-up and residual pest problem.

Managing trash and solid waste in suburbia will have to be a joint effort, or you will be overrun. The trash is going to pile up extremely fast. We do not realize what a burden our waste management teams shoulder for the public.

Laundry, Cleaning, Washing

Washing up after meals and cleaning clothes is not something that will go away with an uncivil society. You will still need to clean up after meals, and clothes will still need to be washed, folded, and put away. The difference is you will not have a dishwasher to load or a washing machine to unload. Things could get incredibly difficult when it comes to clothes and dishes.

A simple stockpile of scrubbing pads, dish soap, and laundry detergent will go a long way when handling these washing duties in a crisis. You can also add things like Borax and baking soda to this stockpile as these are multi-purpose substances that can be used for cleaning, pest control, and even personal hygiene purposes.

In terms of dishes, you could also invest in disposable utensils, plates, and cups, but just remember, while this eliminates a cleaning problem, it creates a waste problem.

Growing Hygiene

While most people do not consider it, a few plants can be grown to help with personal hygiene. The beauty of these plants is that you can save the seeds and create your own little hygiene factory year over year. We are going to focus on two plants in particular and a collection of herbs.

Loofah

The loofah is a remarkably interesting squash that has found its way into the showers of many Americans. While most people think of squash as something you would use in the sauté pan, the loofah is dried and becomes a means of scrubbing your skin. Cloth will be precious, so having the loofah as an option to clean your body and even scrub surfaces in the home is invaluable. Loofahs are also prolific growers, though they do take up a good amount of garden space.

Licorice

We are all familiar with the taste of licorice root. It has been used to cure stomach upset over the ages. The root is very fibrous, and it can be used as a toothbrush. The end can be chewed to break apart the fibers, which will act as bristles, and the licorice scent and oils will help kill bacteria and flavor your breath.

Fresh Herbs

Herbs are powerful and can add both aromatics and antibacterial properties. At the very least, I would recommend growing rosemary, lavender, and oregano. These all have a great fragrance and will affect bacterial growth and infection.

You can add these fresh herbs to soaps, tinctures, salves, and even the soap and deodorant recipes we mentioned above.

No suburban lot would be complete without an SHTF hygiene garden. You can expand on these ideas and look into things like soapnut and other soap alternatives. They are out there. We have only recently limited ourselves to bar soaps and gels, but for centuries, we have used several different methods for maintaining personal hygiene.

Off-Grid Cleaning Methods

We have only been filling dishwashers and loading washing machines for 110 years, but we have been washing clothes for a long, long time! At its most primitive, clothes were beaten with rocks, rubbed with abrasive sands, and washed in the river. Of course, those materials were much different than the materials that we use now. I do not think our polyester blend t-shirts would do well if we beat them with rocks.

The metal washboard carried us from the late 1800s until the wide adoption of electric washing machines, which happened long after their invention in 1907. Investing in a simple washboard as one of these off-grid cleaning methods is not the worst idea.

The washboard can be combined with a few larger buckets and a hand crank ringer. Hot water and soap or baking soda can be used in the first bucket to soak and wash the clothing before rinsing it in a second bucket of clean water. Clothes can then be wrung out and hung up to dry. This older system used three buckets most of the time—one with cleaner and the other two with clean water.

Modern Off-Grid Methods

A clean 5-gallon bucket and a clean plunger can be used to wash small loads of clothes. Your clothes can be soaked in hot water in the bucket, and then your plunger becomes the agitator of the washing system. It would help to have some type of wringer for this system as the clothes will be very wet when you pull them from the bucket.

The Laundry Pod is a larger and more efficient hand crank washing machine that works the same way as a salad spinner. You can agitate the clothes, water, and soap by hand and then spin it to wash and drain the water from the machine. These machines are also very affordable to purchase and store for that SHTF moment where you still need to get the clothes washed.

Washing clothes and dishes is something you will be doing. No matter how terrible the world outside your four walls looks, you are going to need clean clothes to wear and clean plates and cups to eat and drink from to keep the pests at bay.

PEST CONTROL

Pest control will become a crucial issue in SHTF. The general public has no idea how much goes into keeping local pest populations at bay. There is a massive amount of land and water management that goes into simply dealing with mosquito populations. Your city is likely spraying chemicals, too, just to keep these monsters from annoying the population.

That said, you will be less worried about biting mosquitoes and more concerned about the mice and rats that are threatening your food supply. Remember, in an SHTF situation, trash collection is not going to be happening. While you might have a plan to deal with trash, your neighbors may not. This means you will have serious problems with pests of all sizes.

The good news: pest control is an industry. Pests have been widely studied, and mitigation strategies are well known. There is a pest control triangle that is very similar to the fire triangle. If you can affect all sides of this triangle, you will be able to keep pests at bay.

For any Pest Population to Exist, It Only Needs Three Things:

- Food
- Water
- Harborage (a place to nest)

There are many ways that you can affect all of these parts of the pest triangle. The first is to look around your home for leaks and water sources. It only takes a small but reliable runoff to satisfy the needs of small pests like mice and even rats. Simple drainage and filling of holes can eliminate pools of standing water around your home.

These creatures will wreak havoc on your food pantry and food supply if they make a home in your walls and roofing. Once they find their way into the home, they will find the food. If your food is left open and easy to access, things just get better for pests.

Storing food high on shelves and in food-safe containers can go a long way. If you find you have a pest problem, it might also benefit you to store food in jars and Tupperware containers rather than flimsy packaging that can be easily chewed through.

While your pantry is a large food source, pests are often brought to a property because of food access outside the home first. This could be the food in your chicken coop or the area around your trash cans. Cleanliness outside your home is step one. Storing pet and livestock feed in closed containers is vital. Pests love dog food!

Deny them the food, and they will have no desire to learn more about your home. Pest control is a lot like security in that way.

Harborage is another problem that derives from your ability to keep a clean home and garage. Your yard is part of this equation too. Animals use all kinds of things to build their homes. If you look at the average bird nest, you will see that it is composed of all types of things like string, plastic, ribbon, and whatever else the birds can find. If items are unorganized or scattered and areas under decks and sheds are left open, animals will use these materials and these locations to build their homes. Then they can spend more time exploring your home for water and food sources.

Pest control starts with a simple inspection of your home to see if you are contributing to the pest triangle in any way. However, you will need some items on hand if you do find cracks or holes in your foundation, flooring, or other entry points. Denial of entry is huge when it comes to managing pest populations.

- 2-inch lumber for drilling over holes under the home
- Epoxy for filling small gaps (mice will eat through caulk)

- Steel Scrub Pads for plugging smaller holes

If you find that you have an infestation during an SHTF situation, you will need some tools to manage that as well. Most people are queasy about dealing with pests and poisons, but you are going to need to keep your options open as these pests will bring disease and damage to your home and food supply.

- Outdoor Poison Bait
- Indoor Killing Traps
- Small Indoor Poison Stations

The use of poison is dangerous, but it must be available to you. The poison baits used in modern traps are designed to be eaten and scattered. These poisons are not only ingested but are also taken back to dens where the pests live. There, the poison can kill the den and all the pests too.

These same poisons will affect your family. So, be incredibly careful about where you store them, and be sure to check them each day. Do not leave them around open food as the pests could first take the poison before jumping into your food and spreading the poison. If you cannot keep the pests outside of your home, you will have to eradicate them.

KEY CHAPTER CONCEPTS

- Hygiene is one of the most overlooked preps of all.
- You can grow, store, and make many of the things you need to clean your home and yourself.
- Focus on solid waste and human waste. You need a plan for both of these!
- Have some pest control solutions in your storage plan.

9

IS EVERYONE READY?

TEACHING YOUR KIDS EMERGENCY PREPAREDNESS

From the time they can understand what you are saying, you can begin preparing your kids for emergencies. Children are born with an innate survival instinct. When they start walking, you might have trouble believing this because they will get themselves into so much trouble! That said, even babies understand that loud noises and unfamiliar faces can be a problem.

The earliest survival training that you undergo with your kids is to avoid strangers. The idea of 'not talking to strangers' is something we teach our youngest children in society. This is excellent training, and it allows your child to understand the genuine threats that exist in our world.

For some reason, we look at things like teaching kids about strangers and teaching them about inappropriate touching as good parenting. Still, if you teach your young child about self-defense or something like a fire or blackout response, you can be labeled as 'extreme'. To understand how to teach your kids about emergency preparedness, you must first decide what they need to know and stand by it.

Two years ago, if you told your co-workers that you were building a pandemic kit that was fully stocked with a teaching curriculum for your children because a pandemic could shut down schools and stores for an extended period, they would look at you funny. If you told them you were going to talk to your child about the potential of a pandemic in the future and how they might not be able to go to school, they might report you! Know your convictions and act from a position of planning and power, not fear.

At Home

The very basis of teaching kids' emergency preparedness is the creation of a safe place at home. The home must resonate with safety so that kids can grasp the concept of what a disaster or emergency might be like. Sadly, many kids exist in homes that are sheer chaos, and there is no safety for them. Your first and most important task is to provide your child with a safe home.

From there, you can turn them into whatever kind of bushcraft survivalist child you want! In the home, many different things can be learned. From locating specific emergency tools to running drills that are very important to preparedness, your kids should know where certain things are in the home and how to use them.

- Blackout kit
- Bugout bag
- Emergency communications
- First aid
- Emergency food
- Some type of age-appropriate weapon

Home training will make up most of your efforts, so you must take the time to speak to these concepts. Your kids not only need to know where these things are, but they should know how to put them to use. Make it a fun family bonding time instead of strict, regimented training. I cannot emphasize this enough.

Hidden Password Game

A fun game that you can play with your kids is the hidden password game. Create a signal word that you say, and the kids scatter and hide. Turn this into a game that you play regularly. Choose a word other than *hide* but one that is easily recognizable in the home.

Your kids will hide in the best spot they can find, and they will stay put. The password comes in next. This particular password is the only word that will get the kids out of hiding. Explain this at the beginning. Explain that no matter what Mom or Dad say, if they come out, they lose. You can only win the game if you come out when the password is uttered. Kids love this game, and they get a real kick out of scattering and hiding at a moment's notice.

This is excellent training for a break-in or other chaos outside of the home. If your kids are trained to hide at a moment's notice, then you can simply call out your signal word when someone strange walks up on your porch or if you hear something strange downstairs at night.

The password ensures that no one will be able to get them to come out unless they have the password.

THE HOME CULTURE

To do it well, preparedness has to become a lifestyle. If you can integrate things like outdoor adventure, fitness, gardening, archery, cooking, and other activities that promote self-reliance and independence, these things will begin to shape your life. Your kids will start to reflect your preparedness influence. These types of things will start to show up on your television, on your bookshelf, and maybe even in your kids' toy box. The younger you can get them engaged with three-step ahead thinking so that this becomes a normal way of life, the better.

While basic concepts like "stop, drop, and roll" and shelter-in-place can be taught, you want kids to be immersed in a culture of preparedness if you are truly planning for an SHTF situation in your neighborhood.

Another great benefit of living the kind of outdoorsy, homesteader lifestyle is that it introduces your children to real-life threats. If you spend time in the woods, you have to talk about bears. If you are raising chickens, you have to talk about predators. These conversations about predators and dangers will make bigger conversations during SHTF easier for kids to comprehend.

It is very easy to let your kids just drone on in front of screens today. Sometimes you have no control over what your kid is up to because you and your spouse are at work. However, if your home and your time together is spent productively and your home culture is built around being ready and spending time outside, your kids will take to prepping far more quickly.

Drills

At home, drills are one of the most important things you can do to ensure your family knows how to react in an emergency. If you are reading this book, then chances are you are more dedicated to preparedness than the other people in your home. However, you need to drill certain things in your home.

This is a rare annual or biannual practice that should include the entire family, no matter how much they huff and puff. Make it tough but exciting and make them think about their position and how they can both keep safe and help out.

Fire

The fire drill should be conducted at least on an annual basis and should block your main exit and entry points. In other words, you shouldn't be able to walk out of the front door during your fire drill. If a real fire allows for it, then it will be much easier, but do not count on using it.

A house fire isn't just going to burn in the halls and kitchens. If you wake up and find that access to your downstairs is limited, do you have an answer to that? Can you get out of your windows? Do you have some kind of ladder? How about getting pets out of the house?

Your fire drill should not be something everyone in your home is prepared for. You should spring it on the family and maybe discuss it ahead of time with your spouse. There will be a bit of chaos in a real fire, so you want the practice to include that element too. Fire drills at night can be effective, but most importantly, you just want to be sure that everyone knows how to react when the alarms start blaring, and you have to get out!

Shelter-in-Place

The next drill that you should run yearly is the shelter-in-place. This is important for bad thunderstorms, hurricanes, and tornadoes. It touches a bunch of issues, and that is why it is so important.

First, you need to identify your shelter-in-place locations correctly. Great spots are at the center of the home or beneath ground level.

- Basement
- Enclosed Space Under Steps
- Pantry
- Bathroom without Windows

Your shelter-in-place location will need to fit your entire family plus any animals that you want to shelter, too! Sometimes dogs have to be squeezed in tight.

There are also a few things that you are going to need inside your shelter-in-place location. Now, you could create a small bin of these items and leave them inside your shelter-in-place. That makes life much easier. At the very least, I like to have these things inside the room with my family.

- Lanterns or Flashlights
- Emergency Radio
- Kids Entertainment

- Food
- Water
- Small USB Powered Fan (You will get hot in that tight space!)

If you can fit everyone you hold dear and some light gear into this space, then you have yourself a great spot. Be sure you drill staying in there for at least 10 minutes together. This will highlight any pain points that need to be addressed. We remove the bottom shelf in our pantry as this adds dog room and gives them their little space away from our feet!

Break-In

While a home invasion is a much rarer occurrence than a fire or severe storm, it is one of the most traumatic experiences your family can experience. If you are not prepared, you can easily be left to the will of those who have done the breaking in.

Some thefts are focused around a quick smash and grab, while others can turn unbelievably violent. There seems to be an uptick in what I would call Robberies +, which are a combination of theft and assault or even murder.

For your children, they should know what steps to take when they hear something that goes bump in the night. The moves they make will be defined by you and yours, but they should be well aware. Things like secure, predetermined hiding places or heading to your bedroom are great ideas, but they need to be more than just ideas.

The triggers for this move could be anything from something that does not sound right at night, to a knock on the door, to seeing someone in the home. All of which can be terrifying for a child.

Away From Home

The fruits of your labor come into play when your children are away from home. What they do will help you understand whether or not they understand their role in preparedness. When I see polite and helpful children, I see some of the most important players in a disaster. Children like this are often calm and cool in high-stress scenarios. That is the key!

While you are out of the picture, there are some things that you can offer up to your child to ensure they are aware of and effective in a disaster or emergency. One of the simplest is to either have them memorize your address and phone numbers or to keep that info on their person. I prefer memory.

If they are carrying a backpack, there is no reason you cannot outfit them with a simple kit. Of course, you have to be clear with your kids that these items are not toys.

Let's Build a Quick Kit for Your Kids When They are Away From Home:

- Water Bottle
- Flashlight with backup batteries
- Emergency Whistle (good ones are incredibly loud)
- Simple Snack
- First-aid Kit
- Kids Poncho
- Small Book
- Small Wipes
- Cell Phone (big decision for most parents)

You can fit most of these items into a small pencil case so that it will be inconspicuous to anyone who looks in the bag or if your child takes it out to make room for something else.

In Disaster

Perhaps the most important lessons of all come amid disaster or emergency. Here you get to see your kids under the pressure of the unknown. This can make or break them depending on the child, their temperament, and their journey.

One of the greatest lessons anyone prepping to survive SHTF in Suburbia must take into consideration is that the first step is to remain calm. This is very hard for children because they can hardly stay calm on a car ride. When lights are blinking and phones beeping and radios making that crazy emergency alert noise, they get scared.

Remember, you are the living, breathing example of what a calm response to disasters should be. There are no words you can speak that will outweigh your actions in a crisis. You can tell them to remain calm until you are blue in the face, but if you are pulling out your hair, then they will see that and feed off it.

This is why it is so vital that you remain calm too! Disaster specific activities can be a great way to deal with things like storms and power outages. If you reserve a list of activities and games for only when disasters strike, your kids will get very excited when the power goes out, or the storms roll into town. You control the narrative on this, and you can either instill a sense of calm and fun or a sense of fear into them. I chose fun and calm every time!

Enjoying Life

It does not just have to be about preparing for a disaster. Developing survival skills and an understanding of self-reliance can be extremely rewarding. The great outdoors offers a multitude of opportunities.

Take your children into the wilderness, and not just as a vacation. Build the wonders of this world into your life. These are things like mountains, shorelines, highlands, meadows, and wetlands.

Hiking or fishing on the weekends will build something in your children that is tremendous and impossible to replicate. They will become familiar with the natural world; they will be immersed in fundamental survival skills like land navigation, and the lessons just build and build.

Swimming, hunting, and geocaching are other great activities that hook kids on the outdoors. Geocaching is the process of finding small hidden treasures that are placed around our nation and parts of the world by the geocaching community. Your job is simply to use coordinates and find the cache. Some of these caches contain small toys or items that can be traded. Others are simply a small stack of papers that you sign to prove you have found this particular cache. It is a great time and a wonderful way to teach your children about using their skills to search for something.

Our lust for life must be greater than our fear of death. This is not just a prepping lesson to teach your kids but one that will follow them all through life.

THE BIGGEST MISTAKE

If we are going to discuss who is ready and who is not, we need to talk about the single biggest mistake you can make as a person preparing for SHTF in Suburbia. A situation like this is going to cause widespread chaos and likely violence.

You cannot be the sole proprietor of survival knowledge at home. Since you are reading this, you must be the person who focuses most on prepping and survival. Without you, much of what needs to be done would not get done. However, if you make the mistake of holding all the info and not having others to help, you put your family and yourself at an even greater risk.

If you do not share your plans with kids and introduce them to the preparedness culture, they will be helpless in an SHTF situation. The weight of the moment will fall on you, and that might be too much to bear. Sure, you like to think that you will perform when it is all on the line. If your body fails or you get injured, your family will suffer, and no one will have the basic knowledge to get you back in the game.

Violence is rarely one-sided, and if someone attempts to break into your home, you could be wounded. The wound might cost you your life unless someone else in your family knows how to patch you up! Family members need to know how to stop people from bleeding to death!

It is much easier just to do all the work yourself. It is easier to mockup the plans and understand them. To gather the family around and be sure they understand them, well, that takes work. However, it will pay off when the time comes for you and yours to react.

Some family members can bristle at the idea of sitting down and learning about your emergency plans. Sometimes it is simply better to create an effective emergency response plan that they can turn to. The more training you can do as a family, the better. Do not forget, if you are already living an inherently independent lifestyle with a decent interest in the outdoors, that will go a long way too!

You cannot face down SHTF in suburbia by yourself. Nor should you try! Everyone will be safer and better off if they all do their part. Do not make the mistake of shouldering the full burden. It won't end well.

KEY CHAPTER CONCEPTS

- Your home life will dictate much of your child's preparedness.
- Preparing them at home allows them to practice preparedness outside of the home.
- Include your kids in emergency drills.
- Do not make the mistake of keeping all the knowledge to yourself. Your family unit needs to be just that, a unit, a team! This is not a dictatorship.

10

THE BACKUP PLAN

WHEN BUGGING IN NEEDS TO BECOME BUGGING OUT

I n the prepping community, we tend to toss around the word bugout far too liberally. It becomes more of a Band-Aid than an actual resource. That is a problem. Whenever things get too real, there are some preppers out there who just default to the bugout.

The bugout is a massive undertaking that requires investment, planning, and high-level execution to be most effective. It is not just a dot you put on a map and decide you will go there when everything gets squirrely. There are a lot of steps that go into bugging out, and if you are even remotely considering it, you should pay close attention to this chapter.

We will ask some fundamental questions about bugging out and set some very simple but necessary parameters for what you need to bug out effectively.

Can You Bug Out?

A question that many people do not ask themselves is, "Can I bug out?" Not everyone is capable of bugging out, and there are all kinds of reasons why that might be true for you too! There could be circumstances that keep you from bugging out that you have not even taken into consideration.

Your home is your greatest survival investment, remember? Simply emulating all of it at another location is going to be near impossible for most of us. So, you have to be very sure that bugging out is something you want to add to your bag of tricks.

What if you are severely disabled? Is bugging out something you want to deal with? Is it something you are capable of pulling off? There are some situations where you simply cannot bug out, or pulling it off will cause you tremendous pain or hardship.

What about the tens of thousands of Americans who care for elderly parents in their home? Could you figure out how to get your elderly parents to the bugout location? What if you were tasked with getting there on foot? A wheelchair through the woods is as ugly as it gets.

Things like medications, injuries, and illness all affect your ability to bug out. You have to sit down with your family and ask the questions. You have to walk through this bugout process and recognize your weakest links. Obesity is another problem in our nation, and many people who are morbidly obese struggle to walk to the mailbox, let alone head 10 miles down the road with a backpack on.

The good news is, you can overcome a lot if you take the time to plan. There is more to you than you think as long as you can be honest about your shortcomings.

There is an element of risk to bugging out and to everything we do in life. Even the most perfect bugout plan for two fit people, who are well-armed and prepared for success, can go bad. That said, there are some serious hindrances in people's way, and we have to be honest about what we are capable of because once you head out of the home, everything gets real!

Locations Before Bags

The biggest mistake we make when considering the bugout is to buy the bag and the contents before considering the location. It is a big problem! Imagine packing your bags for a vacation that you hadn't booked yet. You do not know where you are going or for how long, but you have your suitcases packed and ready to go. Do you need a bathing suit? Do you need sunscreen? Do you need a sweater?

This is how silly it is to pack your bugout bag before you even know where your bugout location is. Now, do not get down on yourself. You have been tricked into buying that bag and filling it up with gear. You see, the bugout is not just about being prepared and keeping people safe. No. The bugout is also about marketing and making money. There are all kinds of companies out there that are making money off writing posts, making videos, and scaring people into buying things. It is sad, but it is true.

This is how so many of us get conned into buying things we are not even sure we will need. For the most part, the things you buy will help in one aspect of preparedness or another. It is not a total waste. However, the idea that you have packed up the perfect bag without knowing where you are headed is kind of crazy.

So, Where do We Go?

The idea behind bugging out is that you must leave your home because you cannot live there anymore due to threats from the environment, people, or a lack of essential resources. Where you head should be the opposite. You should look for a place where you are safe, there are plenty of resources, and you can survive.

While many people like to believe they are going to bug out to the woods, that is a very tough way to live, and unless you are versed in long term camping, austere living, or something along those lines, you will not be able to last very long in the woods. However, I understand that many people have no other option.

Let's Look at Some Locations to Consider for a Safe Bug Out:

- Raw Land, you own
- Alternate Home
- Cabin
- RV
- Family-Owned Land
- State Park
- National Forest
- Family members home (most people do not consider this for an easy bug out!)

There are lots of options for bugout locations; just be sure you do not start trespassing as that could go bad. Do the easy stuff first. Talk to family about staying with them if you need to bug out. Chances are you have someone who lives in the country, and as long as you are going to do some work and not just be a drain on resources, they would like to have you. Once you have secured a location or a few, you need to start thinking about how you get there.

How do We Get There?

To get to your location, you are going to need to know the route. Everyone is going to need to know that route and how to get to the bugout location. This might be a route that travels highways or backroads.

For many people, once they have a route, they are good to go. They are going to jump in the vehicle and hit the road in an emergency. So, what happens when the road is blocked. What happens when that route is no longer an option?

Because of these situations that could arise, you need to have more than one route to get to your BOL. You could argue that you should have more than one BOL! However, that gets expensive, fast!

At the very least, you should have several routes to get to your BOL. Some of these should be on the road, and others should be on foot. Maybe include some bike routes as even more options. If you cannot get to your bugout location, then it isn't your bugout location anymore!

Avoid major roads when planning bugout routes. Avoid routes that take you over water. There are many obstacles on roads you travel every day that you might not consider until there is a disaster and you have to get through in a hurry.

You also need to consider what neighborhoods your bugout route is going to take you through. You want to avoid driving through or near rough neighborhoods in your city or town. You also need to understand that highly populated areas can suddenly turn into rough areas.

Craft yourself a few bugout routes that are going to get you where you need to be in times of emergency or disaster. Share these routes with your family, give them maps to carry in vehicles, and if it all comes apart, everyone will know where to go and how to get there.

Be prepared to go by vehicle and on foot. The locations and the means of travel will tell you everything you need to know about what you should pack in your bugout bag.

In this next section, we will delve deep into all the things you can store in your bugout bag and how to meet your survival needs while not putting hundreds of pounds on your back. The bugout bag can wear you down if you are not careful.

BUGOUT BAGS AND CONTENTS

Once you get an understanding of your bugout location, you can create an effective bugout bag that will meet all your needs. This will require a bunch of different types of gear and will also take a lot of consideration when it comes to how many people will need bugout bags and to what degree.

Remember, building bugout bags is a very personal process. Let's start with the bugout bag itself. For a long time, it has been assumed that a bugout bag should be huge. It should be the largest possible bag you can find and filled to the brim with survivalist goodies!

If your bugout is a straight shot down a country road for 20 miles, you might not need a bag at all! There is little chance that the road will be blocked, and you are likely to be outfitted with a vehicle that can get around that blockage.

However, if you are bugging out from NYC and you are headed 80 miles west to a secluded area, then yes, you are going to need quite the bag to make that journey; even if you are in a car, that's a long way! So, the conditions of your bugout will largely determine the type of bag you need.

Paratus 3 Day Operators Pack by 3Vgear

A large and affordable modular backpack, this model is one of my favorites to recommend because it is one of the largest bags you can get for the price. If you have a lot to pack, this backpack will take a chunk out of that.

If you have two or more members carrying these bags, you will be able to put a serious camp on your back and outfit people pretty effectively. It has just the serious capacity you may require, and you are going to pay in the hundreds for a similar bag that does what this one does.

This bag is especially effective because you can remove all of the parts and pieces that are affixed to the outside of the main bag. In other words, you can break this bag into parts and pieces. This makes things easier from organization to operations outside of base camp, and even when you need to ditch the larger bag because of a threat or the need to move quickly.

The Paratus features two side pouches with minimal organization and a rapid assault pack at the bottom of that bag. This can be removed and even features a sling that allows you to carry it over your shoulder. This small pack has a much better layout for organization. You could likely get away with this little pack as an EDC bag.

Rapid Assault Pack by Condor

The Rapid Assault Pack is a powerful bag that is built stronger than the Paratus. You can feel it. This bag is more durable, and the price is higher, but you get a lot out of this pack. It is set up in the same style as the Paratus with two side pouches and a small pack nestled under the main storage area. The big difference is all these sections are fixed to the bag.

There are benefits to that, and there are problems with that too! If you are looking for another big bag but not one that is framed, this might be the perfect bag for you. A framed hiking pack is another option, but that is a big undertaking and usually costs over $100.

This is a great bag and, though it costs more than the Paratus, it is still a very affordable bag for what you need in a bugout bag.

Velox II by 3Vgear

If the assault pack style is too big for you, a simpler tactical bag might do you one better! My bag is the Velox II because it answers the call to a number of different things that I need to achieve with it. It can become an effective bag for hiking, trips, get home bag, and even a high-quality bugout bag. It is a great bag.

This bag is set up differently. It is smaller and carried closer to the body. This is one of the things I like most about this bag. You have two main compartments that offer a lot of space for equipment. Then you have a smaller pouch on the top portion of the bag. I use this bag for everything, even fire starting!

Below that small portion, you have another square compartment for storing a few different kinds of things. This area I reserve for beverages, utensils, and other food and drink-related items. This way, I have quick access to fire, forks, tea, and coffee when the need arises.

You can lay your bag out however you like, but these bags are tremendous for what you need. I have put the Velox II through hell and back, and it remains a very tough bag that goes a long way when I need it to.

Incognito Bugout Bags

The downside to all of these bags is the fact that they are all very tactical looking. The look of the bag gives away a bit of its intention. For most people bugging out, that may not be an issue. However, suppose you are in a city or a highly populated and contentious area. In that case, you will not want to give way all of your intentions by having a camo assault pack on with your militarized patches showing clues to your political affiliation and other dangerous information.

Vertx makes some great bags that blend in seamlessly with other bags in a crowd. Their Commuter and Ready-Pack lines are great examples of bags that can stand as a bugout bag but also blend in without anyone ever noticing.

How you manage your bugout bag, and the type of bag you choose is a very big deal. Consider what you need to carry and the type of environments you are going to carry that bag through.

Caches Along the Way

You cannot carry everything, so it is important to use survival caches along your bugout route. These are simply hidden, waterproof containers that can be filled with all sorts of useful resources for the person bugging out. These caches are especially important to the person who is bugging out on foot. They will lighten the load exponentially.

The building of caches is pretty simple once you have the right containers and the resources to go inside of them. Beyond that, you are going to need locations that make sense. Concealment is the key because if they are found, they will be taken.

Let's Look at the Types of Items That Can be Contained in Caches:

- Food
- Water Resources
- Clothing
- Ammo
- First Aid Supplies
- Firearms
- Shoes
- Seeds
- Silver

Hiding caches in the ground is the most common. You will need a shovel and an area where you can turn over the earth and be inconspicuous. You can also hide caches in trees. If they are tall trees or well-hidden trees, your cache can be spray painted to match the bark and hidden.

If you need help finding great hiding spots for your caches, download the geocaching app we talked about in the previous section. After hunting for geocaches for a couple of weeks, you will be much better at locating good hiding spots for your survival caches.

I have seen caches that are stored in the water, too! These can be chained to large roots in an undercut bank or even chained to a deeply sunken post that you also 'install.' Caching can be as creative as you want it to be. It can be as covert as you want it to be. I have even seen things like false rocks used to cache survival items. It gets deep once you get into it.

Rally Points

The best-laid plans, well, you know how they go. Just because you create a perfect bugout plan does not mean that the outside world will go along with it. Rally points are designed to give you an option when the plan falls apart around you.

Mike Tyson was famously quoted saying, "Everyone has a plan until they get punched in the face."

Do you have a plan for when you get punched in the face? If not, then you are going to need to have rally points. Rally points are predetermined locations where your family will meet up when some kind of disruption breaks you up. This could be a group of people, an animal attack, a weather event, or something else.

Rally points can be predetermined, or they can be picked out along your way. You are looking for things that stand out in the distance. Things like cell towers, buildings, rock outcroppings, or other features that are easy to identify from afar and easy to reach.

As you progress on your bugout journey, rally points will change. Keep identifying new rally points as you go so that at a moment's notice, your family can be dispersed and then reconfigured near one of these rally points. There is tremendous potential in that. Getting everyone back together is the only way you can get back to bugging out.

Arriving

After the long journey, you find yourself face to face with a bugout location. You have made it from point A to point B in chaos, despite the odds. Whether you made it there by foot or by car, it does not matter. At that point, all that matters is that you have arrived. Now, it might seem like the perfect time to rush to the front door and dive into your bugout location.

But you have to be very careful about this. There is a bit of a process to follow when you are arriving at your bugout location.

Remember, you might not be the only person who has considered your bugout location as a place to weather the SHTF storm. Someone else may have arrived since the last time you stored important things or visited there, or even since you picked the location based on its advantageous position. If you are careful, you can find out if someone is at your location or not from a distance. That will be the safest way to find out.

There are several things that you want to avoid when approaching your bugout location.

- Walking into an occupied area
- Being seen before you see them
- Being ambushed at your location

Never forget the value of your BOL. If you have invested in this location, someone else could happen by and notice the "value" of the location. Since you are not always at your bugout location, there are times when it can be scoped out by others without you even knowing it.

One great way to know who is checking in on your bugout location is to have motion-activated trail cameras installed on your property. This will catch snapshots of what is moving around your property. Hopefully, you will see plenty of deer and turkey. You do not want to see a bunch of kids or a single person lurking around looking in windows. Of course, this would be great intelligence if you knew this ahead of time.

Let's Look at the Simple but Cautious Approach you Should Take When Arriving at Your Bugout Location:

- Find a vantage point that gives you the best view of your bugout location. This is a place you can find now, so you know exactly where you are going when the time comes. This location should be far enough that you need an optic to see it well.
- Setup a small but straight forward camp which can be quickly set up and broken down.
- Watch this location for at least 4 hours or until

sundown. Traveling to the location in the cover of
night is a huge benefit.

- Clear every room in the home before settling in
  for the night.
- Practice serious light discipline, i.e., do not use
  any flashlights that first night.
- Sleep in shifts the first night to ensure that
  someone is always up your first night in the
  bugout. Depending on how you feel about the
  safety of your BOL, you might want to do this as a
  nightly precaution.

If you make it this far, then you are going to be sitting in
your bugout location. Hopefully, you have chosen an
effective location that offers you all that we have talked
about. As far as I am concerned, this is a success when it
comes to bugout planning and execution.

Why Not Just Live at the Bugout Location?

There is one bugout question that I am asked all the time.
This question is kind of frustrating, but it comes from a
place of misunderstanding. It usually goes something like
this:

"Why can't I just live at my bugout location?"

Neither situation is possible. You cannot just live at your
bugout location because then it is not your bugout
location.

The bugout plan is based on the idea that where you are living right now could become hazardous or untenable. It does not matter if you live in the suburbs of a highly populated city or if you live off a gravel road in the country. Numerous situations could cause either location to become untenable.

Things like earthquakes, floods, radiological disasters, and even simple house fires can turn your "BUGOUT" location in paradise into a wasteland. Where do you go in an emergency if you already live at your bugout location? Where do you bug out to when your bugout location is under attack. Therefore, you simply cannot live at your bugout location. It is impossible because a bugout location is not a permanent residence. It is a plan to seek another living space if your primary residence is threatened or too much of a risk.

While it might sound like a great idea to simply sell your suburban home and move to a bugout location, it is not possible. The BOL is not a permanent situation. Believing you live at your bugout location might be more dangerous than living in the city itself! At least in the city, you could have a bugout cabin in the woods. If your home is the bugout cabin in the woods and you do not have another option when the cabin is knocked down, you are just left with the woods and the cold and whatever else lurks. Do not take this shortcut and make this mistake.

KEY CHAPTER CONCEPTS

- Do not build a bugout bag until you know where you are going.
- Create a few bugout routes.
- Choose the right bag for the job.
- Plan and hide some survival caches if you have a long and arduous bug out ahead of you.
- Understand and identify rally points along your bugout route to keep you and yours together.
- Have a process for inspecting your BOL upon arrival.

CONCLUSION

For years I have been teaching people how to prepare for tough times. With all honesty, I can say that I have never seen a nation more prepared for chaos. While the laundry list of issues reads like a dictionary, it is safe to say that we have every opportunity to see chaos in the suburbs.

We are living through a moment in American history when the very pillars of what holds our Nation up are cracked at the foundation. Now, I am not a fear monger. I could have motivated you with fear throughout this book, but I have always preferred enlightening and informing people and allowing them to see the writing on the wall.

You see the writing, don't you? That is probably what brought you here. Look at all of these chapters as buckets. By this point, you should have a clear understanding of each of these buckets and how you can fill them. Over the next few months, you should focus on filling each of these buckets little by little.

Now that you know how to stock your pantry and store water, you have the skills to sustain your family for months at a time, if not years! Think about the power in that. You also know how to gain the skills to look after your family regarding medical care and first aid. Stopping bleeding and caring for the sick is a game-changer.

This book has pushed you towards a life of self-reliance and independence, and now it is time for you to take action. Now that you have the blueprint, you can start filling buckets and preparing for SHTF in the suburbs.

In many ways, I admire you. You are about to start down one of the most rewarding paths in life. It is the path of fortification and preparedness. You might think you are just fortifying your pantry and your home, but the reality is, you are revealing a better lifestyle for you and yours.

Thank you so much for taking the time to read When Crisis Hits Suburbia. Please leave a positive review if you enjoyed this book. I hope you find the time and the will to act on your preparedness goals.

T. Riley

REFERENCES

Ballard, K., 2020. *The Ultimate Prepper First Aid Kit (Full Supplies List).* [online] The Preparedness Experience. Available at: <https://thepreparednessexperience.com/prepper-first-aid-kit/> [Accessed 22 July 2020].

Brindle, D., 2020. *53 Essential Bug Out Bag Supplies: How To Build A Suburban "Go Bag" You Can Rely Upon.* 2nd ed. p.126.

Bug Out Bag Builder. 2020. *Important Documents To Keep Checklist.* [online] Available at: <https://www.bugoutbagbuilder.com/learning-tutorials/important-documents#:~:text=If%20an%20emergency%20forces%20you,are%20part%20of%20your%20grab> [Accessed 14 June 2020].

2000. *Centers For Disease Control And Prevention.* Atlanta, GA: Centers for Disease Control and Prevention.

2004. *Dietary Reference Intakes For Energy, Carbohydrate, Fiber, Fat, Fatty Acids, Cholesterol, Protein, And Amino Acids (Macronutrients)*. Washington: National Academies Press.

2020. [online] Available at: <https://www.fema.gov/emergency-managers/national-preparedness/plan> [Accessed 17 June 2020].

Garden, H., HowStuffWorks, Garden, Improvement, DIY and Safety, 2020. *Home-Security Tips*. [online] HowStuff-Works. Available at: <https://home.howstuffworks.com/home-improvement/household-safety/home-security-tips.htm> [Accessed 3 August 2020].

Illanes, F., 2020. *9 Critical Essentials For Choosing The Perfect Bug Out Location*. [online] Ready To Go Survival. Available at: <https://readytogosurvival.com/bug-out-location/> [Accessed 8 June 2020].

Redcross.org. 2020. [online] Available at: <https://www.redcross.org/content/dam/redcross/atg/PDF_s/Preparedness___Disaster_Recovery/Disaster_Preparedness/Food_Safety/Food_and_Water-English.revised_7-09.pdf> [Accessed 21 June 2020].

The Prepared. 2020. *Survival First Aid Kit Checklist*. [online] Available at: <https://theprepared.com/bug-out-bags/guides/first-aid-kit-list/> [Accessed 26 July 2020].

The Provident Prepper. 2020. *The Provident Prepper Action Plans | The Provident Prepper*. [online] Available at: <https://

theprovidentprepper.org/the-provident-prepper/>
[Accessed 29 August 2020].

Uspreppers.com. 2020. *Off-Grid Power For Preppers.*
[online] Available at: <https://uspreppers.com/off-grid-power-for-preppers/> [Accessed 12 August 2020].

Walton, J., 2020. *Five Prepper Must-Haves For SHTF Hygiene - Apartment Prepper.* [online] Apartment Prepper. Available at: <https://apartmentprepper.com/five-prepper-must-haves-shtf-hygiene/> [Accessed 18 August 2020].

THE PREPPER'S PANTRY

NUTRITIONAL BULK FOOD PREPPING TO
MAINTAIN A HEALTHY DIET AND A STRONG
IMMUNE SYSTEM TO SURVIVE ANY CRISIS

INTRODUCTION

Let thy food be thy medicine and thy medicine be thy food.

— HIPPOCRATES

When you're prepping for an emergency, one of the most important elements to have is food. The general recommendation is to have at least a few days' worth of food on hand at all times, but what good are a few days if you find yourself unable to leave your home for weeks? Especially now, in the wake of the COVID-19 pandemic, it's become clear that sometimes you simply can't leave your home. Maybe the stores are too crowded and supplies are gone. Or maybe you get diagnosed and have to stay at home for at least two weeks. Or what if some other calamity causes you to have to stay put in your home for weeks or even months?

Being prepared in the event of an emergency is one of the best moves you can make. While we all like to think that nothing will happen to us or our families when we're all cozy in our homes, disaster could strike at any time. Whether it's an earthquake that decimates the infrastructure and cuts off the supply routes, the outbreak of war, or even a pandemic that causes a total lockdown, it's essential to have food on hand. But not just any food will do. Having a well-stocked, healthy, nutrient-rich pantry can make the difference between life and death, depending on how long the disaster lasts.

It's easy to say that nothing bad will ever happen to you, and there's a chance that you'll be right. But there's also a chance that you'll be wrong, and you don't want to be left with only your words of regret to eat. Preparing in case of an emergency isn't much different from buying insurance for your car. You have it in case you need it, while hoping that day never comes. However, the day you get into an accident, you'll know that your initial investment was worth it.

Preparing for the worst isn't about paranoia: It's about being prepared so you and your family are kept safe. You want to go to sleep knowing that if anything happens, you've prepared yourself and your family to the best of your ability. Even if you live in a city, being able to bug in, or stay in place until the danger passes, is essential. You'll need food if you want to shelter in place, making no trips out to find food or other resources.

That's what this book is here for. It's hard to know which foods can be safely kept and which ones you'll need to keep yourself healthy. That's why, in this book, you're going to learn about your nutritional requirements and what you can do to meet them, even when you don't have access to grocery stores.

By this stage, you might think that all this sounds great, but why should you believe a word I say? Well, let me introduce myself. My name is Ted Riley, and I've spent my life learning about survival. It all began when I first entered the Boy Scouts, and my love of learning to survive in this crazy, wonderful world has continued since then. I spent more and more time outdoors, learning to live off the land. The outdoors was like my extended home as I'd swim, make my shelters, and even learned to catch and gut fish with my father.

By the age of 10, my family started traveling for work. My father's unique skills meant he was sent all over the world, and while we didn't want for much, we still found ourselves in situations that weren't the safest. I learned about the value of being able to survive in new environments, how to make my presence known, how to assimilate when necessary, and how to make myself disappear.

You might think that what I experienced in countries like Pakistan is nothing like what you'd face in your daily life, but just take a look around you. In 2020, cities and states in America were calling curfews, initially to slow the spread of a deadly virus, and then to prevent violence from riots across the nation. Every country falls apart at some point. Emergencies happen at some point. War and violence are very real parts of the world. Why pretend otherwise?

My early life experiences encouraged me to settle down in Eastern Oklahoma. Here, my family has a homestead, and every day we're one step closer to self-sufficiency. Part of my motivation for this was to enjoy the satisfaction that comes from creating our world and meeting our own needs. However, part of it was influenced by what I saw growing up.

I don't doubt that we'd be able to survive just about anything, and my children have learned about the importance of self-sufficiency and preparedness. It's taken work, but now, I'm able to go to bed each night safe in the knowledge that, no matter what happens, we'll be able to get through it.

Before settling into my home, I dedicated my life to studying survival, both in the wilderness and in urban environments. I knew this was my calling, and now, I have a new one: to share my knowledge with others and ensure that they too can survive and protect themselves and their families. Are you ready to learn about how to keep your-self and your family alive when the world becomes a more dangerous place? Are you ready to build up a contingency plan in case you can't easily access food? By the end of this book, you will have a better idea of how you can keep your family fed and safe no matter what happens. So, let's get started!

1

PREPARING TO BE PREPARED: THE BASICS OF A HEALTHY DIET, AND WHY YOU SHOULD BE FOLLOWING ONE BEFORE DISASTER STRIKES

Bodies are pretty marvelous creations, and despite popular belief, your body doesn't need food just to keep itself alive. Without the right food, your body can't work effectively. You need to understand which foods matter and which ones will not do much more than to keep your belly full. While not feeling hungry is important, if all you eat are things that will not provide you with the nutrients you need, you won't feel much better in the long run.

Your body needs carbohydrates, fats, proteins, and fiber to function properly. Beyond that, it requires trace amounts of several vitamins and minerals. These micronutrients are used to keep your body functioning properly. Your cells need them to complete their intended functions so your body stays alive.

You're probably healthy now, but do you know how to keep yourself healthy when supplies are limited? What are you going to do if you can't get hold of fresh, healthy produce? When so much of the long-life food available isn't very healthy or conducive to keeping you alive, would you know how to keep yourself and your family feeling well?

Understanding the ins and outs of a healthy diet is crucial if you want to understand how to meet those requirements in desperate times as well as in times of stability. Even though you might be a master at making organic, healthy, balanced meals now, you might not manage so well if all you have are some canned goods and you don't know what to focus on. Now, you're in luck because pre-packaged food is required to be labeled with its nutritional facts. However, if you don't know what your body needs, can you be sure you're meeting its requirements?

The average adult needs somewhere between 2,000 and 2,500 calories each day, depending on how physical they are. Beyond just caloric intake, they must also take in the right macronutrient ratios. You can't just eat 2,500 calories' worth of sugar and expect your body to function properly. Likewise, 2,500 calories' worth of fat or protein won't keep you full and energized. You need to balance them out just right.

Macronutrients

Macronutrients are the parts of food that we commonly think of as the major food components: carbs, proteins, fats, and fiber. These are important in different ratios to ensure that your body works well.

Carbohydrates

Most people hear the word "carbs" and think of sugar. Sugars are often considered unhealthy, but that's a bit of a misconception. While you should limit added sugars and processed carbohydrates, natural sugars are a great way to get a quick energy boost and help you feel ready to take on anything.

Carbohydrates serve as your body's major source of energy. They are the sugars, starches, and fiber you consume when you eat fruits, vegetables, grains, or dairy products. Typically, we categorize these as either simple or complex carbohydrates, depending on how they are broken down by the body. Some diets may recommend that you cut them out entirely, but they are essential to a long-term healthy diet. Your body needs them to continue moving and functioning at the optimum level.

Adults are typically recommended to consume roughly 45–65% of their daily calories through carbohydrates, preferably complex. However, every person is going to have different needs. Let's say you need to eat at least 2,000 calories per day. 1 gram of carbohydrates is roughly 4 calories, so if you need 2,000 calories, eat somewhere between 225 and 325 grams of carbs each day. The National Institutes of Health (NIH) recommends at least 135 grams per day. Diabetics are recommended to limit their intake to only 200 grams, while pregnant women are told not to eat less than 175 grams. We mustn't forget the kids either: Children have different dietary requirements, depending on their ages and activity levels.

The carbs you consume are essential for your nervous system and muscles. They allow your body to keep its activity level normal and regulated without needing to break down muscle or fat. Because they're quick to metabolize, they're easy for the body to use for quick energy.

Not all carbs are good carbs, however, and you'll need to take into consideration whether they're simple or complex. The difference between the two is how quickly your body can break down and absorb the sugars within them.

Simple carbs are those that contain just one or two sugars, such as fructose and galactose, which you can get in fruits and milk products, respectively. These single sugars are known as monosaccharides. Carbs with two sugars within them are known as disaccharides. These are sugars such as sucrose, lactose, or maltose, which are found in table sugar, dairy, and beer respectively.

These sugars all come with other nutritional values, such as fiber, vitamins, and minerals. For example, an apple might be loaded with sugar, but it also comes with vitamins, minerals, and fiber that make them healthier. Refined sugars are little more than the empty calories that are typically associated with weight gain, coming from sources such as:

- Candy bars
- Potato chips
- Soda
- Table sugar
- White bread

Complex carbs are those with three or more sugars, and are typically thought of as starchy foods. Common ones include:

- Beans
- Corn
- Lentils
- Parsnips
- Peanuts
- Peas
- Potatoes
- Whole-grain bread, cereals, and pasta

While all carbs are digested quickly and easily, simple carbs are digested much quicker. They provide a quick burst of energy, but your body also quickly burns through them. Complex carbohydrates take much longer to break down, which means instead of getting the quick sugar high followed by a crash, you'll get sustained energy. This is what you should aim for when looking at what foods to keep in your pantry.

Proteins

Proteins are essential in creating muscle mass in the body, and they are primarily found in animal products, although there are some great vegetarian sources. A single gram of protein is roughly 4 calories, and your body's weight is ideally about 15% protein.

Proteins are made up of amino acids, built from carbon, nitrogen, hydrogen, sulfur, or oxygen. They are consumed and broken down to create more muscle mass. The more muscle mass you have, the faster your metabolism.

Protein also keeps you feeling fuller longer. According to a 2014 study published in *Nutrition*, when people consume high-protein yogurt as a snack, they feel fuller longer than if they had high-fat crackers. The high-protein snack also caused satiety that made them less hungry at dinner. Beyond just providing satiety, protein is also known to improve the immune system, which we'll be addressing in depth in the next chapter. It provides essential amino acids that will help your body's immune system to fend off foreign bodies, while also allowing for the rebuilding and healing of cells.

Protein should make up between 10% and 35% of your diet each day, depending on your activity level, weight, age, and sex. While it's easy for people to get protein throughout their day, most people get it from fatty sources. Lean proteins should be emphasized. There are several important sources of protein that you can enjoy, with many of them also vegetarian. Foods that are protein rich include:

- Beans
- Eggs
- Meat
- Nuts and seeds
- Peas
- Poultry
- Soy products

It's recommended that you consume between 20 and 30 grams of protein per meal. That is the equivalent of 3–4 ounces of meat or 2.5 egg whites. Most women don't get enough protein in the mornings, which can be problematic for both hormone regulation and boosting metabolism.

Fats

Fats get a poor reputation in the dieting world, but they're incredibly important. Fats serve an important purpose: They act as storage for energy. Fat is significantly more calorie-dense than proteins and carbs, with 9 calories per gram. Fats also aid in vitamin absorption, keeping skin and hair healthy, adding insulation to the body, and helping to protect organs.

However, fat must be consumed in moderation. It is recommended that you get 20–30% of your calories from healthy fat sources each day, coming in at around 44–78 grams daily. As essential as it is, too much fat can quickly lead to increased levels of fat in the body as well, which can be detrimental to your health. You can't just skip the fat entirely, and often, low-fat options are unhealthy for you because they're filled up with sugar to make them taste better. But you also need to make sure that you eat the right kinds of fats.

Fats come in several varieties, with some being beneficial and others harmful. Saturated and trans fats are typically regarded as unhealthy, while unsaturated fats are healthier for you.

- **Saturated fats:** Saturated fats are those that are saturated with hydrogen molecules and typically, they come from animal sources. They are usually solid at room temperature, like cheese, butter, and certain oils, such as coconut oil. High levels of saturated fats are linked to higher cholesterol levels, which can put you at an increased risk for cardiovascular disease. They also are high in calories. You should get only 5–6% of your calories (roughly 13 grams) per day from saturated fats, according to the American Heart Association.
- **Monounsaturated fats:** Monounsaturated fats are those that are liquid at room temperature. They are beneficial to the human body, aiding in improving cholesterol levels and protecting the heart. They also may aid in regulating blood sugar and insulin levels, according to the Mayo Clinic. You usually find these in avocados and olives and their associated oils, such as extra virgin olive oil. Despite being healthier, it's important to recognize that you still need to be mindful of how many calories you take in from healthy sources.
- **Polyunsaturated fats:** Polyunsaturated fats are also liquid at room temperature. They've got more than one carbon bond in their fat molecules, which is

how they get their name. They are commonly found from plant food sources like soybeans, sunflower seeds, walnuts, and flaxseeds. They are also found in fatty fish like herring, trout, tuna, and salmon. These forms of fat decrease the risk of cardiovascular disease while also aiding in cell development and maintenance. They also provide essential fatty acids, including omega-6 and omega-3 fatty acids.

- Omega-3s allow for lowered blood pressure and act as anti-inflammatories.
- Omega-6 fatty acids also help the body, improving bone health, benefitting the reproductive system, and promoting healthy skin and hair. However, in excess, omega-6 fatty acids can be inflammatory.
- **Trans fats (trans fatty acids):** These fats occur naturally, especially in meat or dairy, but typically are only present in small amounts. They are most often found in processed foods, baked goods, refrigerated dough, coffee creamer, fast food, and margarine. They are linked to heart disease and weight gain, and in 2013, they were declared by the FDA to no longer be safe. Artificial trans fats are banned in the United States. Don't bother stocking up on too many of these.

Fiber

Fiber is an essential macronutrient, but not for the same reason as the others. The other three—carbohydrates, protein, and fats—are broken down to provide energy for the body. However, fiber cannot be digested to provide energy. Rather, it is used to aid the digestive system, and you get health benefits from it.

Fiber prevents us from becoming constipated, and the US as a whole misses out on the right levels of fiber needed for health benefits. The average American adult consumes only 15 grams of fiber, while it's recommended that you should consume significantly more. Women are recommended to consume at least 25 grams up until the age of 50, at which point the recommendation drops to 21 grams. For men, 38 grams is recommended, and at age 50, that recommendation goes down to 30 grams.

Fiber is comprised of roughage: the fibers found in fruits and vegetables that you can't digest. You might think that if they can't be digested, why bother eating them at all? The answer is simple: because you want to move food along in your digestive system. If you want to get the waste out of your body, you need to have something that can move that waste through once you've digested enough of the food. That comes from the fiber. As you bulk your diet up with fiber, the waste can be excreted quicker.

It's also essential if you want to keep yourself feeling full. Fiber feels heavy in the stomach, and because of that, it can help you feel full and lose weight, as it cuts out the need to snack. Beyond just helping to keep you regular, fiber protects from a wide range of chronic diseases, such as heart disease, cancer, and type 2 diabetes.

It is essential for feeding the healthy Microbiome in the intestines. In many heart foods this is called probiotics. A healthy Microbiome is responsible for maintaining a healthy immune system.

You can bulk up your food with added dietary fiber from many easy sources. For example, you can expect to get plenty of fiber from grains, fruits, and vegetables.

Micronutrients

Your body also needs vitamins and minerals to stay healthy. We commonly refer to these as micronutrients, and while they're needed in smaller quantities than the macronutrients, they're still essential to your health and wellbeing. Your body cannot create these micronutrients itself, so it must get them from other sources.

Vitamins vs. Minerals

Vitamins are crucial for your body's functions, from producing energy to regulating the immune system or blood clotting. Minerals are used for your body to grow, balance fluids, and keep your bones dense. The vitamins that you consume are organic compounds that plants and animals make, which may be altered or broken down by heat, acid, or air. You absorb these vitamins and minerals as you eat, allowing your body to function.

Minerals

Your body requires a combination of macrominerals and trace minerals to function properly. Macrominerals are required in higher quantities, while trace minerals are required in smaller quantities.

Macrominerals

- **Calcium:** This allows for the creation of bones and teeth, while also aiding in muscle function and the contraction of blood vessels.
- **Chloride:** Typically found in table salt with sodium. It aids in fluid balance and helps to create digestive juices.
- **Magnesium:** This aids in over 300 enzyme reactions, and also helps to regulate blood pressure.
- **Phosphorus:** This aids in the formation of bones and cell membranes.
- **Potassium:** This is an electrolyte that helps balance and regulate fluids in cells, nerve transmission, and muscle function.
- **Sodium:** This is an essential electrolyte that allows for fluid balance and controls blood pressure.
- **Sulfur:** Every living tissue requires sulfur, and it's a part of the amino acids methionine and cysteine.

Trace minerals

Your body needs fewer trace minerals, but they're still essential for many purposes.

- **Copper:** This is necessary for connective tissue formation and helps your nervous system and brain to function properly.
- **Fluoride:** This helps bone and teeth to develop.
- **Iodine:** This aids in thyroid functionality and regulation.
- **Iron:** Iron allows for oxygen to be processed by muscles and aids in creating certain hormones.
- **Manganese:** Manganese works in aiding carbohydrate, cholesterol, and amino acid metabolism.
- **Selenium:** This helps with thyroid health, while also being essential for reproduction and as an antioxidant.
- **Zinc:** This is necessary to help with healing, immune function, and normal growth.

Vitamins

Vitamins are essential and come from many natural sources. You'll find them in many healthy foods. Some animals can produce certain vitamins, while others need to get them from food sources. They are organic compounds that will help keep you healthy. Some are fat-soluble and others are water-soluble. Your body can store fat-soluble vitamins for future use, but it can't store water-soluble vitamins for very long.

Vitamin A

Vitamin A is also known as retinol. It's fat-soluble and essential for your eyes. Without enough vitamin A, you may suffer from night blindness. You can get it from foods such as:

- Apricots
- Broccoli
- Butter
- Cantaloupe
- Carrots
- Collard greens
- Eggs
- Kale
- Liver
- Milk
- Pumpkin
- Spinach
- Sweet potatoes

Vitamin B

Vitamin B is water-soluble and comes in several forms with different names:

- **Vitamin B1 (Thiamine):** This vitamin produces enzymes to break down blood sugar. You can get it from foods like yeast, pork, sunflower seeds, brown rice, asparagus, cauliflower, and potatoes.
- **Vitamin B2 (Riboflavin):** It's necessary to help the body develop cells and aid metabolism. You can find this vitamin in foods like asparagus, bananas, fish, yogurt, meat, eggs, and chard.
- **Vitamin B3 (Niacin):** Also known as niacinamide. Your body requires it so cells can grow and work.

You can get it from eggs, salmon, milk, beef, tuna, leafy greens, broccoli, and carrots.

- **Vitamin B5 (Pantothenic Acid):** It helps with creating energy and maintaining hormone regulation. It's found in meat, broccoli, avocado, whole grains, and yogurt.
- **Vitamin B6 (Pyridoxine):** It is necessary for the creation of red blood cells and can be found in chickpeas, liver, bananas, and nuts.
- **Vitamin B7 (Biotin):** It is used to metabolize proteins, fats, and carbs. It also helps to produce keratin, which your body needs to create hair, nails, and skin.
- **Vitamin B9 (Folic Acid):** It is essential to make DNA and RNA. It's especially important for women of child-bearing age, as early deficiencies can affect fetal nervous systems before women even know they're pregnant. It's recommended to be supplemented for this reason, even if you're not pregnant. It's commonly found in leafy greens, liver, peas, legumes, fruits, and many fortified grain products. If you're a woman, or live with a woman who may become pregnant, keeping foods fortified in folic acid is essential.
- **Vitamin B12 (Cyanocobalamin):** It's necessary in order to create a healthy nervous system. It can be found in fish, shellfish, meat, poultry, milk, and eggs.

Vitamin C

Vitamin C, or ascorbic acid, is a water-soluble vitamin that our bodies use to help with wound healing and bone formation. It aids in producing collagen, and builds strong and healthy blood vessels, while also boosting the immune system. It plays a vital role in the absorption of iron, and is also antioxidant in nature. Without it, you can develop scurvy, which causes problems with healing and tissue growth, and can result in the loss of teeth. You can find vitamin C in most fruits and vegetables, but they have to be eaten raw, as cooking destroys it.

Vitamin D

Vitamin D is known as ergocalciferol or cholecalciferol. It's a fat-soluble vitamin that your body needs to help it develop bones. Without it, you may suffer from softening bones or rickets. You can get vitamin D through sun exposure which triggers your body to produce it. Alternatively, you can get it from fatty fish, beef liver, eggs, or mushrooms.

Vitamin E

Vitamin E is referred to as tocopherol, and it is also fat-soluble. It is an antioxidant, reducing and preventing oxidative stress. It can be found in kiwis, wheat germ, eggs, almonds, nuts, vegetable oils, and leafy greens.

Vitamin K

Also called phylloquinone, vitamin K is fat-soluble and is crucial for blood clotting. Without it, you may bleed too much. It can be found in leafy greens, pumpkin, figs, parsley, and natto.

Choline

Choline is a bit of a special case. Although not classified as a vitamin, it is a nutrient that your body needs. Your body can produce some choline, but you also have to consume it in order to stay healthy. This essential nutrient is organic and water-soluble, but is neither a vitamin nor a mineral. It is commonly grouped with the B vitamins because it is similar in what it does; it's necessary for liver function, metabolism, muscle movements, brain development, and regulating the nervous system. It's essential for optimal health. You can get it from liver, eggs, cod, salmon, broccoli, and cauliflower. Eggs are an excellent source, supplying roughly 25% of your daily requirement.

Recommended Daily Intake

NUTRIENT	INFANTS 12 MONTHS AND UNDER	CHILDREN 1-3 YEARS OLD	ADULTS AND CHILDREN AGED 4 AND OLDER	PREGNANT AND LACTATING WOMEN
BIOTIN	6 MCG	8 MCG	30 MCG	35 MCG
CALCIUM	260 MG	700 MG	1,300 MG	1,300 MG
CHLORIDE	570 MG	1,500 MG	2,300 MG	2,300 MG
CHOLINE	150 MG	200 MG	550 MG	550 MG
CHROMIUM	5.5 MCG	11 MCG	35 MCG	45 MCG
COPPER	0.2 MG	0.3 MG	0.9 MG	1.3 MG
FOLATE	80 MCG	150 MCG	400 MCG	600 MCG
IODINE	130 MCG	90 MCG	150 MCG	290 MCG
IRON	11 MG	7 MG	18 MG	27 MG

NUTRIENT	INFANTS 12 MONTHS AND UNDER	CHILDREN 1-3 YEARS OLD	ADULTS AND CHILDREN AGED 4 AND OLDER	PREGNANT AND LACTATING WOMEN
MAGNESIUM	75 MG	80 MG	420 MG	400 MG
MANGANESE	0.6 MG	1.2 MG	2.3 MG	2.6 MG
MOLYBDENUM	3 MCG	17 MCG	45 MCG	50 MCG
NIACIN	4 MG	6 MG	16 MG	18 MG
PANTOTHENIC ACID	1.8 MG	2 MG	5 MG	7 MG
PHOSPHORUS	275 MG	460 MG	1,250 MG	1,250 MG
POTASSIUM	700 MG	3,000 MG	4,700 MG	5,100 MG
RIBOFLAVIN	0.4 MG	0.5 MG	1.3 MG	1.6 MG
SELENIUM	20 MCG	20 MCG	55 MCG	70 MCG

NUTRIENT	INFANTS 12 MONTHS AND UNDER	CHILDREN 1-3 YEARS OLD	ADULTS AND CHILDREN AGED 4 AND OLDER	PREGNANT AND LACTATING WOMEN
THIAMINE	0.3 MG	0.5 MG	1.2 MG	1.4 MG
VITAMIN A	500 MCG	300 MCG	900 MCG	1,300 MCG
VITAMIN B6	0.3 MG	0.5 MG	1.7 MG	2 MG
VITAMIN B12	0.5 MCG	0.9 MCG	2.4 MCG	2.8 MCG
VITAMIN C	50 MG	15 MG	90 MG	120 MG
VITAMIN D	10 MCG	15 MCG	20 MCG	15 MCG
VITAMIN E	5 MG	6 MG	15 MG	19 MG
VITAMIN K	2.5 MCG	30 MCG	120 MCG	90 MCG
ZINC	3 MG	3 MG	11 MG	13 MG

Chapter Summary

In this chapter, we went over the importance of your diet to your immune system, while also emphasizing what your body will need so you can prep accordingly.

- The average adult will need between 2,000 and 2,500 calories each day.
- The main macronutrients your body needs are carbohydrates, proteins, and fats, which should all come from healthy sources.
- Your body needs fiber to regulate itself and help with digestion.
- There are several micronutrients that your body needs; the vitamins and minerals are taken in from your food.

2

FIGHTING FIT: EAT FOR IMMUNE HEALTH TO PROTECT YOU FROM HEALTH DISASTERS

Y ou only have one body, and you need to protect it to the best of your ability. You know that there are certain things you need to do in order to keep yourself safe. You wouldn't, for example, jump off a cliff and expect to come out of it unscathed. You understand that jumping from some sort of height would likely cause you some sort of harm. You need to make sure that you're safe. What you rarely think of, however, is that you also need to make sure that you're healthy internally as well.

Your body is built to survive. It's able to overcome most challenges that come its way. If you eat something that is not good for you, you're probably in for a few bad days, but your body will recover. If you get sick, you'll usually be able to kick it, so long as it isn't too bad. If you get a cut, your immune system is likely to be strong enough to fend off infection. But your immune system is only good enough to do so if you set it up properly. Support your body if you want that immune system in tip-top shape.

THE HUMAN SECURITY SYSTEM: THE IMMUNE SYSTEM

Your immune system is composed of organs, cells, and chemicals that work in harmony to fight off infection. They all work together to kill microbes that could pose a risk to your body. From bacteria to viruses and foreign bodies, your body uses the immune system to treat problems. Understanding how your immune system works will help you understand what you need to do to support it. Together, the components of your immune system function as a security system to fend off invaders.

White Blood Cells

At the heart of your immune system are the white blood cells. These are created in your bone marrow and are found within the lymphatic system. The white blood cells are transmitted through your body, traveling in the blood and throughout the tissue. They identify microbes that have entered your body to attack them. When your body detects microbes, the white blood cells then send lymphocytes, among other cells, to the source to destroy the microbes and prevent an all-out infection. Without this initial response, your body wouldn't be able to fend off bacteria, viruses, fungi, or parasites, and they'd be able to spread until they took over your body.

Antibodies

Antibodies are used to fend off microbes or any toxins that may be produced by them. Your antibodies will recognize antigens on microbes. Antigens are essentially signatures on the outside of the microbe that allow for antibodies to recognize their presence. Then, upon matching to the antigens, they can identify the toxins or microbes as a foreign body. At that point, they are marked for destruction, and the rest of the immune system tackles it.

Lymphatic System

The lymphatic system is a system of several delicate tubes that spread throughout the body. These serve many important roles, such as managing the fluid levels in your body and responding to bacteria, cell products, or cancer cells. The lymphatic system also works to absorb some fats from the intestines. It is comprised of several essential parts, including:

- Lymph nodes (sometimes called glands), which trap microbes. You may notice them swelling as they collect microbes in the event of infection.
- Lymph vessels, which are the tubes that allow lymph to flow throughout your body. Lymph is a clear liquid that washes through your tissue and is filled with white blood cells.
- White blood cells (also known as lymphocytes).

Complement System

The complement system is an amalgamation of the proteins that work to support the work of the antibodies.

Thymus

The thymus is an important gland in your chest, found between your lungs and right behind your breastbone. It's an essential part of the lymphatic system, and makes T lymphocytes, sometimes called T cells. These T cells can fend off infection.

Spleen

The spleen is an organ that filters your blood. In filtering it, it's able to destroy old, damaged blood cells and also removes microbes that may have been trapped by the immune system. It can also create antibodies and lymphocytes to aid in the support of the immune system.

Bone Marrow

Bone marrow is found within your bones and creates blood. It produces red and white blood cells, while also creating necessary platelets, which are used to clot the blood.

Skin

Your skin is the largest organ in your body, and serves an essential purpose: It creates a waterproof barrier that also secretes an oil used to kill bacteria. Most microbes cannot penetrate the skin if there is not a wound or other opening for them to enter.

Lungs

As you breathe in and out, you pull air into your lungs. That air is filled with many microbes from around you. These microbes would have easy access to the body if the lungs didn't have some protection. They've got mucus within them to trap any foreign particles, and within your lungs you also have cilia, small hairs that work to force the mucus out of your body as you cough.

Digestive Tract

The digestive tract is also lined with mucus. This mucus contains antibodies that protect you. In addition, the acid in your stomach is fatal for most microbes.

Other Important Defense Mechanisms

Your immune system isn't the only line of defense you have against microbes. While it's an essential part, your immune system is more like the security guard to catch anything that slipped through the gate. The other important defense mechanisms are the deterrents to keep the microbes from entering.

Other Common Defenses

Your body also uses other defenses to prevent bacteria from building up. Your bodily fluids are typically designed to protect you. Skin oil, saliva, and tears work to flush out bacteria and are antibacterial to lessen the risk of infection. You flush your urinary tract and bowels regularly, which also helps to force any microbes out.

Fever is also a common defense and immune system response. When you get ill, you might notice that you end up with a fever. This is because your body is trying to kill off the microbes while also creating conditions that are more favorable for your body to repair any damage.

LIFESTYLE FACTORS FOR IMMUNE HEALTH

Now that you know how amazing the body is and what important functions it performs, you need to understand what lifestyle choices benefit and damage your high-performing body. If you want a healthy immune system, one of the easiest ways that you can achieve it is by ensuring that you keep up with your health. Enjoying a healthy body helps to support your immune system. When you've got a healthy body, there's a good chance that most immune responses will not be a big deal. There are other factors that you can remember to keep your immune response healthy as well. By ensuring that you live a healthy lifestyle, you're much more likely to keep a healthy immune system.

Don't Smoke

One of the most frequently stressed rules for keeping a healthy immune system is to remember that smoking is awful for your health. As you smoke, you damage your lungs, which, as we discussed, is one of the more important barriers you have between your body and microbes.

Exercise Regularly

Exercising helps to keep other parts of your body, like your heart and lungs, healthy. It also keeps the blood pumping throughout your body.

Eat Healthily

A healthy diet can provide you with everything you'd need to support your immune system. The vitamins and minerals you consume will help to prepare all essential parts of your immune system so you're ready to go when the need arises.

Maintain a Healthy Weight

Keeping your weight healthy means that your body is healthier overall. You'll have a lower risk of stroke, heart disease, and diabetes, amongst other dangerous conditions. Studies have also shown that too much fat can trigger your immune system to behave erratically.

Drink Alcohol in Moderation

When you drink, you impair your body's immune system as well, except the damage lasts far longer than the intoxication does. You risk harming the lungs, for example. Your gut bacteria can be killed off as well, which may also boost the risk of infection. Alcohol can be inflammatory in the gut. Because your body has to prioritize processing what you drank, it can't focus on the immune system. And, because it causes your sleep to worsen, you weaken your immune system even more. If you're going to drink, make sure that you're drinking in moderation. Binge drinking, in particular, can be an immense problem, and research has shown that if you regularly drink over 14 drinks per week, or over five or six drinks in one sitting, you will directly suppress your immune system.

Quality Sleep

Your body uses sleep as a chance to take care of itself. It is essentially the maintenance period that allows the body to put more effort into the immune system. So when you're sick, you're usually sleepier and sleep for longer. During sleep, energy can be directed directly to the immune system. As you rest, there is a boost in cytokines, which are associated with the immune system and inflammation. Even when you're not sick or hurt, the cytokine production goes up at night, likely to boost adaptive immunity so you can trigger your immune system to remember antigens in the future. By making sure you get quality sleep, you can ensure that your body's immune system is in top condition.

Good Hygiene

Cleanliness is essential if you want to have good hygiene, but too much cleanliness can be problematic as well. You're constantly in contact with millions of germs, but by practicing good personal hygiene, you can protect yourself. Just washing your hands regularly is a great way to protect yourself from infections. You don't need your home to be spotless and bacteria-free. Some bacteria are not very harmful at all and can also keep your immune system functioning normally.

Mindfulness for Stress Reduction

Stress is harmful to your immune system, as precious resources are redistributed elsewhere. When you're stressed, the level of lymphocytes is decreased, which then puts you at an increased risk for illnesses. This is because stress causes cortisol to build in your body, and too much cortisol causes more inflammation. This is where mindfulness comes into play. Mindfulness helps to reduce your stress, which drops your cortisol levels and allows your body to be healthier.

Micronutrients and Immune Health

We've already gone over several of the most essential micronutrients your body needs to function. Many of those are directly related to the immune system, including the following:

- **Carotenoids:** Carotenoids boost the immune system because they can be converted into Vitamin A.
- **Copper:** Copper is important in the creation of

red blood cells and helps the immune system to maintain its nerve cells.

- **Folic Acid:** Folic acid encourages cell growth and development to heal wounds and tissue. It also boosts the production of antibodies.

- **Iron:** Iron allows for the production of white blood cells and slows the production of bacteria.

- **Probiotics:** Your entire gut system is lined with a system of bacteria and other microbiota that influence how your body works. Probiotics work to suppress bad bacteria while boosting good bacteria. They also have been shown to create natural antibodies and boost immune cells.

- **Selenium:** Selenium reduces inflammation and is powerful in protecting against respiratory infections.

- **Vitamin A:** Vitamin A regulates antibacterial and anti-inflammatory immune responses.

- **Vitamin B6:** Vitamin B6 is used for the production of white blood cells and T cells. It also allows for the creation of the protein interleukin-2, which directs white blood cells.

- **Vitamin C:** Vitamin C possesses antibacterial and anti-inflammatory properties and stimulates the production of antibodies and white blood cells.

- **Vitamin E:** Vitamin E is found in higher concentrations in immune cells and regulates the number of natural killer cells. Deficiency impairs the immune system.

- **Zinc:** Zinc reduces inflammation, while also serving as an antiviral. It has been shown to boost natural killer cell activity.

Whole Foods to Boost Your Immune System

If you want to boost your immune system, one of the best all-natural methods of doing so is to include as many healthy foods as you can in your daily diet. Consider the following as staples if you can get your hands on them:

- **Almonds:** Almonds and other nuts are full of vitamin E, which is a fat-soluble vitamin. With just ½ cup of almonds, you can get your total daily quota of vitamin E.
- **Bell Peppers:** Bell peppers, especially red ones, have a massive amount of vitamin C and beta carotene. They are one of the best sources of vitamin C.
- **Broccoli:** Broccoli is loaded with vitamins A, C, and E, plus it's filled with fiber. However, it loses many of its benefits when it's cooked: Eat it raw or lightly steam it.
- **Garlic:** Garlic not only tastes great, but it is also known to have a high concentration of allicin within it. This sulfur-containing compound is believed to aid in fighting off infections, and garlic was commonly turned to as an antibiotic in ancient civilizations.

- **Ginger:** Like garlic, many have turned to ginger to help reduce illness. It decreases inflammation in the body.

- **Grapefruit:** Grapefruit, like most citrus fruits, is high in vitamin C. Your body cannot store Vitamin C on its own, so you need to get enough of it each day to remain healthy.

- **Green Tea:** Green and black teas are both loaded with flavonoids, which are antioxidants. They are also packed with L-theanine, an amino acid that is believed to help produce T cells.

- **Kiwis:** Kiwis are full of essential elements, including folate, potassium, vitamin K, and vitamin C. These nutrients help to create white blood cells and to support the rest of your body's functions.

- **Papaya:** Papaya is full of vitamin C, with double the daily recommended value in just one medium-sized fruit. It also contains papain, which has anti-inflammatory effects, and is rich in folate.

- **Poultry:** Poultry is a fantastic choice if you want to boost the immune system. Chicken and turkey are full of vitamin B6. And, when you use the bones to create a bone broth, you'll also get beneficial gelatin and other nutrients that will boost your health.

- **Shellfish:** Shellfish is rich in zinc, especially if you choose mussels, lobster, crab, or oysters. However, make sure you don't eat too much: More than the recommended amount of zinc can inhibit your immune system.

- **Spinach:** Spinach is high in vitamin C, beta carotene, and many antioxidants. It is incredibly healthy if you eat it raw, or with as little cooking as possible.
- **Sunflower Seeds:** Sunflower seeds are loaded with phosphorus, magnesium, and vitamins B6 and E. They are also rich in selenium, with one ounce of sunflower seeds containing nearly half of your recommended daily allowance.
- **Turmeric:** Turmeric is a widely used anti-inflammatory that is rich in curcumin. Curcumin is believed to be an immune booster and has some antiviral properties.
- **Yogurt:** Yogurt, especially Greek yogurt, is full of good bacteria that help your digestive system. Look for "live and active cultures" on the label, and choose plain varieties over other kinds. You can sweeten it with a bit of honey and fruit.

We rarely think much about what we do day to day and how those actions may affect our health. However, everything that you do in your life, from how much you sleep to what you choose to eat, will affect your health. Your immune system is your first line of defense against any harm or illness that may come your way. Living a healthy lifestyle is the best way to keep yourself healthy. This means emphasizing healthier foods, sleeping well, and exercising regularly.

Chapter Summary

In this chapter, we discussed the importance of lifestyle on your immune system. Some of the most important points include:

- The immune system protects the body from illnesses, and is therefore essential for ensuring that, in an emergency, you are healthy.
- Diet and lifestyle both directly influence the immune system.
- Foods rich in certain vitamins and minerals are essential for your immune system's health.

3

AN ESSENTIAL GROCERY CART LIST FOR HEALTHY SURVIVAL

Grocery stores only keep roughly three days' worth of food on hand. One thing that COVID-19 showed was that as soon as some shelves look a little empty, the panic shopping begins. People are terrified of not having enough food on hand because, without the right amount of food, how are they supposed to feed and provide for their families? How are they going to ensure that their children have enough food to eat?

The supply chain is not very efficient at dealing with delays. You don't want to be caught with empty shelves when an emergency happens, and you don't want to have to beat the rush as everyone tries to get to the store at the same time. In the event of an emergency, most people will only have a few days' worth of food stocked and they will have no other choice than to flock to the stores.

With the basics under your belt and an understanding of what your body needs, you can start planning the essentials for your food stores. Because there are so many foods that you'll want to keep stocked up, you may need to do multiple shopping trips to get everything in the right quantities. One of the most important elements of putting together a prepper's pantry is understanding that you will not go out on one big trip and get everything you need all at once. There are a couple of reasons for this, which we will discuss later in the chapter.

As you read over this chapter and the next, you may realize that some items on the second list make more sense to stock up on sooner rather than later. Customize how you choose to shop based on what you have available to you according to your location, needs, and circumstances.

This chapter will introduce you to several important aspects of stockpiling. It will include the importance of reducing the costs of your purchases, while also exploring the idea of setting up a garden for yourself to ensure that you've got plenty of food on hand. Even if you have limited space available, there are methods you can use to garden within your space constraints.

We will address the essential FEMA recommendations for disaster preparedness, as well as go over a list of the best foods that you should prioritize in your stockpile. By the time you've finished reading, you will have a pretty good idea of what you should start stocking up on and why.

Reducing Costs with Bulk Buying

Shopping to stock your home is not likely to be cheap, especially if you have a large family to take care of. However, by shopping well, you should be able to keep the prices down. When you buy in bulk, you're able to shave down some costs. This is because bulk quantities of food use less packaging. You also get a discount for bulk quantities. Even if your family doesn't need things in bulk, you can still break them down and package them in smaller rations. For example, imagine you buy a big, 20-pound bag of rice. You will be able to break it down into much smaller increments, or you could keep it in one large bucket. For storing food, you have a lot of options.

Consider some of these tips for reducing the cost as you begin your stockpile:

Check Flyers Regularly

Stores usually change their prices weekly, so you're likely to see fresh foods that you may want to buy in bulk come on sale in different time frames. For example, maybe you are stockpiling chicken. That chicken may be $2.99 per pound this week or $1.59 per pound next week. If you were only trying to buy enough for your family of four to eat a couple of meals in a week, you might not think much of buying 3 pounds for $8.97 today instead of waiting two days and making an extra trip to buy it for just $4.77 when it goes on sale again. The additional $4.20 may not be worth the effort and cost of gas to go to the store again.

However, when you run that math again with larger quantities, such as if you wanted to stockpile 50 pounds of meat, the difference is much more pronounced: at $2.99/lb, you're going to spend $149.50 on that meat. However, if you were to go back a few days later for the cheaper price, you'd spend just $79.50. The difference is $70. At that price point, it's probably worth making a repeat shopping trip. Depending on how close you are to the store, you could ride a bicycle and take a cold bag, and squeeze in some more exercise on the way.

Pay attention to the ads and flyers as you shop and plan your trips. If possible, you could even shop on the day before your local store runs a new ad. Usually, you can preview the sales by waiting until 24 hours before the next ad starts so you can compare the two to figure out what you should buy at which point in the week. It takes a little planning, but once it becomes the norm, those savings add up.

Search through Coupons

Another great way to save some cash is to pay attention to the coupons offered to you by the store. There's a good chance that you can save cash on some items when you do this. It may not be the most efficient way of saving money, but if you're determined to cut down on costs, this is another strategy to include—especially if you wait to use the coupons until they can be used in tandem with the weekly sales.

Stick to the List

You might start seeing other foods and things that you think are worth picking up, but not adhering to a list is usually how shopping trips end up costing significantly more than you intended to spend. By going to the store with a plan in mind and sticking to buying only what you had on your list when you entered the store, you can help to reduce your bill. This is because when you stick to your list, you're able to ensure you're getting the best price possible for an item before you choose to purchase it, by waiting and then cross-comparing with other stores.

Check Several Stores

Before committing to purchasing something, it's a good idea to look through the weekly ads of several stores and shop at multiple places. Sometimes, the prices may warrant stopping at several stores instead of just shopping at one.

Check the Price per Unit of Everything

The price per unit is a way that you can compare the prices to see which size is providing you with the most for the least amount of money. Before you choose to buy anything, always compare the price per unit. Usually, you get a better price per unit by buying in bulk, but this is not a hard and fast rule. Sometimes, smaller quantities are cheaper.

GARDENING FOR YOUR FOOD STOCKPILE

If land is no issue for you, you might establish a garden. Using a garden to add to your food stockpile is a great way for you to be certain that you've got fresh food. The food that you grow can then be canned and preserved, or frozen, to make sure that you've got additional food available to you. If you've got plenty of space available, certain foods that will last longer in your pantry can be gardened readily.

You may live somewhere that growing food year-round is entirely possible. You may even grow indoors, using hydroponics and grow lights, or in a greenhouse that will help you grow food even when the temperatures are too cold outdoors. However, these aren't always workable options for all people, especially when you're in an urban or suburban area. If you've got a plot of land and you're not doing much with it at the moment, creating a garden that can sustain you is a great way to ensure that you're stockpiling food at very little cost to you.

As you stock your pantry and freezer with produce, the best thing you can do is select foods that are easier to store because they keep for months when kept cool and dry, or because you can pickle, can, or freeze them.

Vegetables that can simply be stored in cool, dry places include:

- Dried beans
- Garlic
- Onions
- Potatoes
- Pumpkin
- Shallots
- Sweet potatoes
- Winter squash

Vegetables that may be canned easily in sealable glass jars include:

- Asparagus
- Beans
- Beets
- Carrots
- Cabbage
- Corn
- Peas
- Peppers
- Pickled onions
- Pickled cucumbers
- Potatoes
- Tomatoes
- Winter squash

If you want to stock a deep freezer with the vegetables you've grown, you can grow crops such as:

- Asparagus
- Broccoli
- Brussels sprouts
- Cabbage
- Carrots
- Cauliflower
- Corn
- Eggplant
- Mushrooms
- Onions
- Peas
- Spinach
- Squash
- Tomatoes (when processed)

We will address how to store vegetables later in the book. However, with so many options available to you for the storage of your vegetables, having a garden of your own could be a valuable way to create your stockpile at home.

Gardening in Small Spaces

Even if you've got less space available to you than you'd like, there are ways you can garden in smaller spaces with little trouble. By focusing on using the space that you have, you will enjoy the benefits of gardening, even if it's on a smaller scale.

Vertical Gardens

Vertical gardens are those that primarily grow upwards. This is done by growing on a vertical plane instead of a horizontal one. Typically, several planters are placed slightly on an angle so you can grow several tiers of something in a row. These usually work well for plants that grow somewhat smaller, such as some greens, herbs, carrots, and other small vegetables.

Raised Beds

Raised beds allow you to create a small area dedicated solely to gardening. Usually, they are in sizes like 2'x4' or 4'x4', and you can fill them up with soil, allowing you to grow even if you live somewhere that doesn't have very good ground for growing, such as if you have a small patio with little soil.

Container Planting

If you don't even have the space for a raised bed, there are plenty of containers you can plant in. Many plants can be grown in containers, including fruit trees. You can grow, for example, a pot of tomatoes and pick them throughout the season. You could grow a container of peas or carrots, or just about anything else. Most plants can be grown in a container, as long as you're willing to care for them properly. Often, because container planting involves so much less space than other forms of gardening, you'll need to be mindful of how you choose to care for them. They will need to be watered and fertilized more often, but you can still get plenty of produce from them.

Potted Fruit Trees

Potted fruit trees often do well, especially if you select dwarf varieties and you keep them trimmed. You'll be able to get plenty of fruits from them, however, so don't discount them for their small size. Just keep in mind that many fruits require at least two trees of the same species to properly fertilize and fruit.

FEMA RECOMMENDATIONS

So how much food should you have on hand? This depends on what you're trying to prepare for. Do you want to ensure that you've got food just in case of a storm, or are you trying to prepare for another wave of massive lockdowns? The answer will be based on that. While most preppers will strive to have six months to a year of food on hand, the current recommendation from FEMA is at least three days' worth of non-perishable food on hand at all times, which is a good place to start and build from there. In particular, they recommend that you have:

- At least three days' worth of non-perishable foods
- Foods your family will enjoy eating, especially if you have picky children
- Foods that meet all special dietary requirements

- Foods that won't make you thirsty, such as dried foods or foods high in salt

In particular, they recommend items such as:

- Canned juices
- Comfort foods (in moderation)
- Dried fruits
- Dry cereals
- Granola
- High-energy foods
- Infant foods (if applicable)
- Non-perishable milk (pasteurized)
- Peanut butter
- Protein and fruit bars
- Ready-to-eat canned goods (fruits, vegetables, and meat, with a manual can opener on hand)

Because you have no way of knowing whether whatever emergency comes your way will include power outages or other such disasters, it's always a good idea to ensure that you've got foods that will not need to be prepared. Of course, it's important to have other foods on hand as well.

Why You Should Have at Least 30 Days' Worth of Food

While FEMA provides a general guideline for short-term emergencies, what happens on a larger scale? What if you can't get to the store? What if there is a long-term disaster? Wuhan, China locked down for 76 days because of

COVID-19, with strong limits on who could go outdoors and when. The quarantine was severe enough that people were stuck at home, and when they could get out, stores were often short on supplies.

Three days is a good start to a stockpile for immediate emergencies, but if you worry that you or your household will be stuck at home for a longer time, having significantly more is a good idea. You'll want to start your stockpile with the intention of having 30 days' worth of food and water on hand at all times. Once you have your 30-day supply, it's a lot easier to build on your stocks and slowly build up your stores.

You might think this sounds easy: Couldn't you just buy a bunch of crackers, soup, and rice and call it good? While you would probably survive, you wouldn't be doing your health any favors. You want to make sure that you've got 30 days' worth of nutritious, whole foods that will keep your body healthy even when you can't get out and shop as normal. If you don't plan well, you could wind up with an unsustainable diet that leaves you and your family feeling sick and miserable. You can prevent this relatively easily if you take the time to plan well.

This is essential, especially in this day and age. Anything could happen. The world is teetering on war, with new conflicts seeming to arise every year as others appear to go away. We are in the midst of a massive climate change that could decimate crops. There is the possibility of an earthquake destroying transportation infrastructure. When the supply line falls apart, it will take a significant amount of time to get it working again. What this means for you is that you need to have plenty of food on hand at any point in time.

Canned Meat and Fish

Protein is essential to your body, and if you don't have enough of it, you're going to struggle with ensuring that you've got everything you need to stay healthy. When you select canned meats, it's important to choose grass-fed when possible, and to choose high-quality products that are going to keep you full and nourished. They may not taste as good as fresh or frozen, but in a pinch, they will help you survive, and that's what this is about. For a month, you will probably want to keep around 35 cans of various meats on hand, assuming you have a family of two or three. If you've got a larger family, you may need to double this, as one can only contains about three servings.

Chicken

Canned chicken is easy to find at any supermarket, often in varying sizes of cans. As we discussed, chicken supports the immune system while also reducing inflammation, which helps you to avoid illness and gives you extra support when you're sick. Vitamin B6 will also aid in the development of healthy red blood cells.

Tuna

Tuna is a rich source of omega-3 fatty acids, as well as other fats and oils. Tuna can also be dressed up in many meals, making it quite versatile. If you buy it packed in oil, you keep the flavor and have some extra fat available to use too.

Salmon

Like tuna, salmon is great for providing omega-3 fatty acids. It is also rich in selenium. Salmon is usually a bit more expensive than tuna, however, so make sure that you plan accordingly.

Red Meat

Red meats will provide you with plenty of zinc, which you also need for your immune system. When possible, find grass-fed options.

Canned Vegetables

Canned vegetables are a substantial source of vitamins if you can't find them fresh. It's a good idea to prioritize getting starchy vegetables, such as root veggies and sweet potatoes, as they'll provide you with more calories per ounce than many other options. They're also usually still quite rich in vitamins and minerals to keep you healthy. You'll need around 40 cans, at a minimum, to last a month. You should get whatever you and your family will eat, with an emphasis on:

- Asparagus
- Carrots
- Mushrooms
- Spinach

Canned Fruits

Fruits are an essential part of your diet, and you can usually stockpile them relatively easily in canned form. If you have access to refrigeration, you can refrigerate the leftovers of larger cans and buy the #10 cans, which contain 25 servings each. You and your family will enjoy one to two servings per day relatively cheaply in this manner. Ideally, you'll choose a variety for the most health benefits, but in particular, you want to make sure you have canned grapefruit in there somewhere for its immune-boosting properties.

There's a big debate around whether you want to purchase fruits packed in syrup or juice. A lot of preppers support the idea of buying in syrup as it has a higher calorie content with the additional sugar provided. However, to emphasize and prioritize health, it's better to select fruits that have been canned in their juices instead.

Honey

Honey is a great sweetener with medicinal properties. It is used commonly in teas to boost immune system support, and in medical emergencies, its antibacterial properties can help promote wound healing if you have no other options available to you.

When stored correctly, honey never goes bad. Keep it dry and cool, and you'll be safe. You can buy this in bulk and use it slowly, using it in place of sugar or to add some flavor to oatmeal or yogurt.

SALT, HERBS, AND SPICES

If you were to only eat unseasoned food from cans, you'd probably get sick of it pretty quickly. With no variety, you're bound to get bored. This is where salts, herbs, and spices come into play. You want to make sure that you've got plenty of all three on hand.

Salt for Food Preservation

Salt, in particular, will never go bad when kept dry, and it can add flavor to just about anything with a quick sprinkle. You can get it incredibly cheaply, and it provides essential sodium that your body requires.

Salt can also preserve your food. It's recommended that, in addition to table salt, you have pink Himalayan salt on hand. This salt, although more expensive, is rich in trace minerals that your body needs.

Herbs and Spices

Many herbs and spices also provide you with plenty of health benefits on top of flavor. In particular, try to keep turmeric, ginger, and cinnamon on hand. Not only are they incredibly flavorful to make your food more enjoyable, but they're also jam-packed with benefits. Ginger and turmeric support the immune system, while cinnamon is known for controlling blood sugar and having anti-inflammatory properties.

Garlic

Garlic can be kept for a few months in a pantry or some other cool, dry place. However, if you're hoping for something to last longer, you can buy it dehydrated in a powdered form, pickled, frozen, or canned. All varieties will add a massive amount of flavor to any dish, while also allowing you to benefit from the immune boost.

Hard Cheeses

Cheese is a great option for adding flavor, calories, convenience, and even some health benefits. Cheese has been popular for millennia, and it's worthy of a place in the prepper's stockpile. However, only certain cheeses are suitable for long-term storage. Cheeses come in either soft, semi-soft, or hard options. Hard cheeses are suitable for long-term storage because they have had their moisture extracted. Then, when freeze-dried or dehydrated, it can last even longer.

Hard cheeses can outlast the canned goods in your pantry, so long as they're stored well and they're unopened. Hard cheeses you can keep on hand include:

- Cheddar
- Gouda
- Parmesan
- Romano

You'll want to ensure that there is wax coating the cheese to ensure that moisture cannot get into it and cause it to go bad. With no way for moisture to get to the cheese, there's not much risk in keeping it. Some cheeses are aged for decades before they are even sold, so aim to keep a lot of these options on hand. You could also choose powdered cheese to mix into pastas and potatoes or coat meats, or even cheese in a can or jar.

Cereals

Having some cereals on hand is a great way to ensure that you can get a quick boost of energy, so long as you get the good stuff. Now's not the time to run out and stockpile sugary cereal: It's time to choose foods that you know are going to do your body some favors without making you feel ill along the way. Plus, cereals are a cheaper substitute for many other foods you could buy. Try to stock up at least five big boxes to ensure you've got enough. Your cereals should be:

- Whole-grain varieties with no added sugars.
- From a variety of different grain bases to ensure you're getting all the nutritional value you need.

Many cereals these days are fortified with many of the vitamins and minerals people are deficient in, so while cereal may not be the healthiest option for you, it's also not the worst thing you could eat. And, by adding wheat germ, you can fortify the cereal with more fiber, vitamin E, protein, folate, magnesium, zinc, selenium, and manganese.

Canned Soups

Canned soups may not be the most nutritious option for you, but they last a long time, making them a prepper's favorite. When you have canned soups in stock, they can provide a great emergency backup if you run out of other food. Make sure that whatever soups you choose, you emphasize the healthier ones with higher vegetable content and many ingredients to ensure that you're getting a variety of vitamins and minerals.

Nuts and Seeds

Nuts and seeds are calorically dense and loaded with healthy fats and energy. You can get plenty of nutrients just from nuts while filling in the bulk of your calories, or you could choose to mix them with oatmeal or cereal for an additional crunch. You can use them in many forms. However, it's recommended that you prioritize both almonds and sunflower seeds. If you can, select them in bags rather than jars.

Apple Cider Vinegar

Apple cider vinegar is antimicrobial and also commonly used to help reduce cholesterol, manage diabetes, and lower blood sugar levels. It's good for gut health, and may even aid in weight loss. Because of how it is processed, it is full of many probiotics, but it is quite acidic and should be consumed diluted in water.

Vinegar may also treat wounds, nail fungus, lice, warts, and ear infections, and it can also help preserve food for longer. Having a bottle or two on hand in your pantry is strongly recommended.

Leavening Agents

There's a good chance that you'll want to make bread in an emergency situation, and if you want that bread to rise, you'll need leavening agents. The most common are baking soda, baking powder, and active dry yeast, which has a longer shelf life than the fresh stuff. Keeping these on hand means that you should be able to make many baked goods with little trouble.

Butter

Butter is essential to many cuisines, and let's be real: it tastes good, too! Plus, the health benefits are worth it. Not only is it full of calories, which you'll need for energy, it's also rich in many other essential vitamins and minerals. If you can, get grass-fed options and store them in your freezer to lengthen the life span.

Shopping for your stash of food can be intimidating, especially if you're already on a budget. However, you don't have to buy everything all at once, and you don't have to buy exactly what's on this list. What has been provided here are general guidelines to help you piece together a stockpile that will suit your family's needs. Use this list to plan your shopping to build up little by little.

Chapter Summary

In this chapter, we went over the first wave of what you should have in your pantry and why you need it.

- Stockpiling doesn't have to be expensive if you play your cards right and shop smarter.
- You should have at least 30 days' worth of food stocked up in order to be prepared for any disasters.
- Your stockpile should contain an assortment of canned fruits, vegetables, meats, herbs, spices, fats, nuts, and grains.
- If you want to be able to keep your supplies topped up, gardening is a good way to supplement your stockpile.

4

BULK SHOPPING FOR LONG-TERM STORAGE, SURVIVAL, AND OPTIMUM HEALTH

You might think that your canned goods will be enough for your family to get by on, and you might be right, but you're probably not going to be getting the balanced diet that your body requires if you rely on cans alone. You still need to have a stockpile of the essential macronutrients found in foods such as rice, beans, lentils, and oatmeal to ensure that you can get the caloric content you need without going hungry.

This chapter will essentially supplement the high-calorie and nice-to-haves that you'll want to keep in your pantry.

These foods will probably come in much larger packages, and you'll most likely need to break them down to store them. Otherwise, you risk having an entire bag contaminated if something goes wrong, and when you're talking about large amounts of food, that can be devastating.

You'll most likely want to shop from bulk wholesalers or online to get larger packages and save some money.

The biggest mistake I see people making is seeing a prepper pantry list and buying all the items, even if they don't like them. So just remember that this is a guide: Only buy food that you and your family both enjoy and eat regularly.

Rice

Rice has been a human staple for centuries for a reason. It's easy to produce, easy to cook, and can fill you up rapidly. It can also be stored long-term with little problem. The most economical way to buy rice is to buy it in 40-pound bags, which you can then pack into buckets to protect it from bugs or rodents that might find it easy to chew through the bags.

Brown rice is higher in nutritional content and fiber than many other options. However, it doesn't last as long as white rice. It's a great option to keep on hand for fiber or health reasons, but also stock white basmati rice, which is healthy and will last longer.

Beans and Lentils

You can buy beans in 5-gallon buckets already packaged for you, but you can usually get a discount if you buy the large bags and move them into buckets yourself. Ideally, you'll have several types of beans to get a wider range of nutrition. Beans and lentils offer a significant source of energy and vegetarian protein, and if you're worried about running out of them, you can sprout them rapidly to get your stock going again, especially if you've got space to garden.

Oatmeal

Oatmeal can also be purchased in bulk. A 5-gallon bucket contains around 222 servings. If you don't want to buy in bulk, a normal container usually has around 30 servings, so for a family of four, you'll want to buy at least four of them for a month. Oatmeal is also much more filling than many other breakfast option. You can even flavor it with honey, fruit, nuts, or anything else, if you want additional staying power and to make it enjoyable.

Oatmeal is highly regarded thanks to being both beneficial to the immune system and having a high fiber content. That, paired with the slow release of energy you get, thanks to oatmeal being a complex carb, makes this a great option for a stockpile.

Pasta

Pasta is a substantial addition to many meals, and you can add tomato sauce easily to pack a nutritional punch. When you keep pasta, look for dried varieties, which have very little moisture content which allows them to be kept long-term. Ideally, you'll select whole-grain varieties to get the best nutritional value out of them. You can buy these in boxes or bags and store them. Try to have at least

5–10 boxes on hand. You can usually find them in bulk packages online or in warehouses.

Sugar

Sugar doesn't offer many nutritional benefits. However, what it has is energy. While it shouldn't be a staple that you consume all the time, it is helpful in cooking and baking, and it is quite effective in an emergency when you need something to provide enough calories. Sugar can be stored easily, and you can buy it in bulk. Storing it in 5-gallon buckets is the perfect way to keep it safe.

Dehydrated Milk and Eggs

While you'll hopefully have access to milk and eggs in most situations, if you find yourself locked down for longer than a few weeks, you may end up running out of them. Eggs can usually keep for about a month in the fridge, or much longer if you crack and freeze them like ice cubes, but milk is usually only good for a short period before it goes bad. This is why having dehydrated milk and eggs on hand is a good idea.

Dehydrated eggs usually come in powdered form, and by adding some water to them, you can create an egg mixture that you can use for scrambled eggs. You could also toss them in as powder while baking for significant results. Because of the nutritional value of eggs, it's a good idea to include them in your stockpile.

Milk is great for calcium, and by having powdered milk on hand, you can add some water to it and have the benefits you'd get from drinking milk in a cup. You could use this for cooking as well.

Powdered Whey

Sometimes referred to as whey protein, this is a staple for many bodybuilders because of its high protein content. It can be mixed into drinks to not only flavor them, but also to provide a boost of nutrition. If you're low on protein, adding this to your milk is a great way to fortify it. You can usually find powdered whey in gallon-sized containers and it comes in many flavors.

Drink Mixes

Water is essential to drink to ensure you're healthy, but sometimes, people get bored with it. It's a good idea to have other options on hand as well, such as tea and coffee. Coffee is an excellent caffeine source, and if you're already used to drinking it, you probably don't want to run out of it and deal with caffeine withdrawal. Coffee is also known to be good for the heart, in moderation, and is rich in immune-boosting antioxidants.

Teas typically infuse water with many medicinal properties. In particular, you want to focus on:

- **Chamomile:** Chamomile is the classic tea people turn to when they've got a cold, and for good reason. It's been used for centuries to aid the immune system while also providing relief from cold symptoms. It also helps you to relax. It is commonly served with honey, which also brings soothing benefits.

- **Echinacea:** Echinacea, sometimes referred to as purple coneflower, is a popular tea that was used regularly by Native Americans. These days, it is an herbal treatment for the cold or flu. It may help with inflammation and migraines as well.
- **Ginger:** Ginger tea transforms the antimicrobial benefits of ginger into drinkable form, boosting your immune system. This tea is sweet and spicy, but it's delicious.
- **Hibiscus:** Hibiscus teas are typically filled with antibacterial and antimicrobial properties to help aid in fending off illness while boosting health. It's also rich in iron, antioxidants, and vitamin C.
- **Lemon balm:** Lemon balm smells lemony and delivers significant benefits. It is used for boosting mood and cognitive function, while also boosting your immune system. It is commonly used to relieve nausea, headaches, and menstrual cramps, making it a great tea to keep on hand.
- **Peppermint:** Peppermint tea may be drunk on its own, or as an ingredient in an herbal blend. The mintiness is perfect for soothing a sore throat, and it is rich in antioxidants, also offering antimicrobial benefits.

- **Rooibos:** Rooibos tea is a traditional African tea that is quickly becoming more popular worldwide. It is flavorful and caffeine-free, while also boasting a high antioxidant content.
- **Sage:** Sage tea is known for being laden with anti-inflammatory and antioxidant compounds that may also aid in wound healing. It also is rich in vitamin K.

Oils

Oils are typically used for cooking, but some offer very good health benefits as well. Coconut and olive oils are both highly recommended. Most of the time, rich, hearty flavors come from fat content, and most meals require you to use some sort of fat, whether oil or butter. Having oil on hand is essential for your stockpile. Keep in mind that oil has a limited lifespan: Olive oil, for example, doesn't last nearly as long as you'd think, so make sure you're constantly pulling from your stockpile and cycling through new products. It is only good for between 12 and 18 months, at which point it goes rancid. Keep an enormous bottle on hand at all times, but to avoid waste, don't go too crazy on your stockpile.

Extra virgin olive oil is unrefined, meaning it is of higher quality. It is higher in monounsaturated fats that have been linked to better heart health. However, keep in mind that it has a low smoke point, which means it can't be used for cooking at very high temperatures.

Coconut oil lasts longer, but should be used in moderation. It is high in saturated fats, which is okay if you're not eating too much of it. It is still a healthy option, full of antioxidants, and it is highly versatile. It can be used for cooking, as a lotion, and to clean and condition hair, amongst other things. It is also more tolerant of higher cooking temperatures. You can find this in 5-gallon buckets to stockpile.

Flour

Flour is essential for baking unless you can't tolerate the gluten within it. Having flour on hand will be required for most people, however. You'll need this for baking, making easy meals like pancakes, or even for making your pasta, which is much easier than you'd think if you're in a pinch.

When you select your flours, select a variety. It's always a good idea to have some all-purpose flour on hand, but you also want to keep whole-grain flours as well. You can grind down your oatmeal into oatmeal flour as well.

However, keep in mind that flours are easy to ruin. A bit of moisture will cause them to spoil quickly. Flour should be stored carefully, somewhere airtight and waterproof, with oxygen absorbers. We'll talk more about this later.

Households should have roughly 50 pounds of flour per person for a year-long supply. If you want enough for a month, you'd want between 4 and 5 pounds per person.

Potato Flour

Potato flour is another good option to have on hand. Typically, it's made from the entire potato, which provides you with plenty of benefits. It is often used to stretch regular flour, or you can use it to bake with as well. It's a common thickener when making sauces and gravies, thanks to the starch.

Dried Fruits

We've already touched on canned fruits, but it's a good idea to keep some dried fruits on hand as well. You can buy them in buckets or large cans, and many varieties come with a lot of benefits. Raisins, for example, are full of protein, iron, fiber, potassium, and vitamin C. However, keep in mind that dried fruits often have higher concentrations of sugar since they've been dehydrated and lost much of their bulk. It's very easy to eat too much sugar if you're not careful. Select several types of dried fruits for the best benefits.

Freeze-Dried Chicken

We discussed the benefits of canned chicken in Chapter 3. In freeze-dried form, it includes many of those same benefits, and you can buy this in bulk just as easily. It is often sold in large cans, and by adding boiling water to the chicken, you can rehydrate it to enjoy when you need it. You can buy this in large #10 cans.

Having a fully-stocked pantry is essential. It's strongly recommended that whenever you shop, you keep up with your pantry, always ensuring you have at least one, but preferably up to six months' worth of essential ingredients on hand. Many of these foods can be used regularly, like rice, flour, and oatmeal. Other foods should only be kept on hand for emergency occurrences, such as powdered eggs or milk. Ensuring that you have a well-replenished pantry will keep you healthy and provide you with plenty to fall back on in times of shortage.

Chapter Summary

In this chapter, we finished going over foods that should be stocked in a pantry at all times for a one-month reserve of food.

- Grains such as rice, oatmeal, and flour should be stored well and kept for a source of carbohydrates.
- Herbal teas can be highly beneficial for medicinal purposes.
- Baking supplies, such as powdered eggs and milk, as well as oils, will help stretch out the meals.
- Dried foods, such as fruits and chicken, can help save space and boost the longevity of food.

5

STORING DRY FOODS: EVERYTHING YOU NEED TO KNOW ABOUT CONTAINERS

Once you start stockpiling your food, you'll probably notice that there's a lot of dry foods that need to be stored. Storing dry foods isn't as simple as just tossing them in the containers that they came in into your pantry. You need to make sure you protect them from light, insects, rodents, oxygen, and moisture.

When foods that are low in fat and moisture are stored properly, they can be stored for much longer than you might think. Wheat from 4,000 years ago was found in an Egyptian tomb, and it was still edible. This was because it was stored properly.

Since the whole point of storing food is to protect your family if you cannot access normal grocery shopping for an extended period, you want to make sure it is protected. Without the proper care, you may find that the foods you thought you could rely on are no longer good. Most packaging lasts for about a year, but if you want to keep foods for longer, you'll want to ensure that they have been cared for the right way.

Whether you're packing grains or legumes, there are a few simple steps you can follow to ensure they're suitable candidates. These are:

1. Choose high-quality dry foods that contain less than 10% moisture and are also low in oil content, such as white rice.
2. Select the right container for the food, the space you have, and your preference.
3. Choose the best method to prevent insects from infesting the container.

While you might be a bit intimidated by all of this, it's not as hard as you might think. As you get more familiar with the options, choosing the right one becomes almost intuitive. By following these guidelines, you will be able to keep your food safe so you know you can rely on it when it's time.

As you read through this chapter, you will be introduced to several key topics that will assist you in storing your dry foods. We will first cover what makes your storage choices effective. Then we will go over the most common options: Mylar bags, cans, PET bottles, plastic buckets, and glass jars. We will address how to treat your containers in several ways, and finally cover how you can store your food to keep it safe.

WHAT MAKES A CONTAINER EFFECTIVE?

Food containers must be effective, or you're just wasting your money. If you want to ensure that you're choosing the most effective containers, you need something that's going to prevent your food from spoiling. Most foods will spoil because they're contaminated with something. Typically, this is air, chemicals, insects, light, moisture, rodents, temperature, or time. Now, most of these can be mitigated in other ways. Time is controlled by rotating your stores regularly. Temperature and moisture are eliminated by using a cool, dry pantry for your storage. Chemical contamination is avoided by using only food-grade products to store everything. This leaves your container needing to combat against just four of the biggest spoilers of your food: oxygen, light, insects, and rodents.

Blocks Oxygen

The air you breathe contains roughly 21% oxygen, which allows it to oxidize many compounds in food. It also allows for both insects and bacteria to grow. By removing or displacing oxygen, you can help boost the shelf life of the foods you choose to store. This means that your most effective containers will have some way of blocking airflow from entering. Throwing an oxygen absorber into the container will also be useful for longer shelf life.

Blocks Light

Light can cause changes to the physical and chemical properties of your food. In particular, it allows for food to deteriorate rapidly and causes the degradation of nutrients. It can also degrade the packaging, so if you think you can get away with storing your rice in a bucket that doesn't allow light to enter, you're wrong: The container will still degrade. The best thing you can do is ensure that where you place the container is dark.

Blocks Insects

Insects would love nothing more than to get into the stockpiles you set up. Once they invade, there's going to be no way to decontaminate the food they get into. Insects will enter your grain stores if you keep them in their original packaging, which is why it's such a good idea to store them in something else.

The most common pests that you're likely to run into are weevils, beetles, moths, and ants. They'll do whatever they can to get into your food. They will go from egg to larva to pupa to adult, and it's difficult to eliminate them once they're able to spread. The best thing you can do is to store your food somewhere oxygen-free, which will deprive the insects of necessary air and keep your food safe.

Blocks Rodents

Mice are troublesome, as they can chew through foil pouches and Mylar bags rapidly. They can even chew through plastic buckets if they're determined to do so. Rats can be even worse: They can even get through metal containers if they're determined enough. If you've got rodents, there's a good chance they're going to target your food store. You will need to keep the environment clean and free from rodents. If they're able to chew their way into the bag, they will contaminate your food stocks.

TYPES OF CONTAINERS

Mylar Bags

Mylar bags are made of multilayer laminated plastic and aluminum. Because the food is separated from aluminum by a food-grade plastic layer, there is little risk of contamination. These bags are effective at protecting food from moisture and insects, but they allow for a small amount of oxygen to enter, and they are not rodent-proof. If you want to use Mylar, it's usually a good idea to place those bags into a bucket of some sort to protect them from rodent damage.

Typically, these bags can last up to 5 years, or 20 if you add oxygen absorbers and vacuum seal them. Each gallon of food should use one 300 cc oxygen absorber or 2,000 cc oxygen absorbers per 5-gallon bucket.

Make sure that when you use Mylar bags, you use a heat-sealing device to seal them entirely. If you want to vacuum seal them and secure them using a traditional vacuum sealing device you already have, you can do that too. This requires a bit of creativity, but if you know what you're doing, you can make it work well.

Mylar bags are typically smooth, while vacuum-sealing bags have textured sides to allow channels to be created for the vacuum sealer to suck the air through. By taking a few snips out of your bags, you'll be able to create those channels on your Mylar bag as well. Put two small snips, maybe 1 inch by 2 inches long, on each corner of the Mylar bag, with maybe a ½ inch sticking out the top. Place it into your vacuum sealer, and allow it to suck out all the air. This will take longer than you'd normally expect vacuum sealing to work since there will only be two small channels to use, but it should suck out all the air. At that point, you can use the heat seal setting. Do this twice, and your bag should be secure and ready to go.

Mylar bags should be kept in some other container to prevent them from coming into direct contact with cement or walls. Keep in mind that these bags don't stack well, so they can be a bit of a mess to store well. Your best bet is to store them in large 5-gallon bags, and place these in large square buckets.

Keep in mind that foods with over 10% moisture content risk developing botulism in a low-oxygen environment, so make sure that you only pack dried goods, such as rice, beans, pasta, oats, flour, and sugar. Freeze-dried foods will also do well, but you want to avoid foods rich in oil or moisture.

Cans

If you need to store foods that are low-oil content, dry, and shelf-stable, cans are a great option. However, you must make sure that there is an enamel coating between the food and the metal to keep it food-safe. Cans are traditionally kept in most stockpiles. However, make sure that you have a manual can opener if you choose to stock up in this manner.

Like Mylar bags, it's recommended to use low-moisture foods to prevent reaction with the metal. While a lot of liquid foods may come in cans, they are not suitable for longer-term storage. When possible, dry foods should be stored with oxygen absorbers, except for sugar.

Unlike Mylar bags, however, these can prevent all oxygen from entering the cans. They can rust on the outside, though, so you want to keep them somewhere without moisture. They should not be kept in direct contact with concrete. Typically, you can use a rolling rack to store your cans. Just make sure you label them so you can tell what's in each can.

A #10 can holds 3 quarts and is good for 2.8 pounds of rolled oats, 3 pounds of macaroni, or 5.5 pounds of pinto beans. It may store other foods as well, and you can open them in much smaller amounts than if they were stored in large buckets.

Polyethylene Terephthalate (PET) Bottles

Polyethylene terephthalate (PET) bottles can be good options if you're running low on other types of storage. You should only use PET bottles if you're storing dry goods, however, as they don't provide much of a moisture barrier.

To identify which bottles you have that are PET, look for the number "1" in the recycle symbol. It may also say "PETE" or "PET" underneath the symbol. These bottles should have a screw-on lid, which should also have a plastic or rubber seal. For example, 2-liter soda bottles are made in this manner. You can reuse these; just make sure they're cleaned and dried well. If you've ever used the bottle for non-food purposes, don't reuse it.

You can store rice, corn, beans, and wheat in these bottles for a longer-term period, or you can use them short-term for other foods as well. If you are storing long-term, use one oxygen absorber packet per bottle. Keep in mind that these options must be kept protected from light and rodents. These options aren't as efficient as Mylar or canning, but they are still effective in a pinch.

Plastic Buckets

Using large plastic buckets is another great option, but you must make sure that they are food-grade. They must also be free from other food items. If you've used them for non-food items in the past, don't use them. You can either store food in its original packaging for added protection, or you can choose to use the bucket itself to store things with liners.

Buckets are typically the recommended options for storing food long-term in larger quantities, but keep in mind that oxygen can enter them. It's a good idea to use Mylar bags to line them. Then, make sure you store them off the floor without stacking more than three buckets on top of each other in order to protect the seals.

Grains, flour, sugar, and other dried foods store well in these containers. They are also among the least expensive options for sealing. Just keep in mind that you should only choose food with gaskets in the lid seals.

Glass Jars

If you want to store smaller quantities of something, using glass jars is one of the most effective ways to do so. Their smaller sizes make them convenient, and they can be reused several times, so long as you don't accidentally drop and break them. They are both air and watertight, making them quite efficient, and rodents can't chew through them without significant difficulty and injury. However, because glass is transparent, you need to keep it protected from light in order to prolong the life of your food.

TREATMENT OPTIONS

Before you store anything in a container, one of the most important things you can do is make sure that there's no chance of an insect infestation. Eggs are often too small for you to see, and you may not notice if there are a few tiny insects in a big bag of rice as you pour it into a container. The best thing you can do is use some sort of treatment to protect your food stores. Typically, this is done through a method that will help to reduce oxygen content, which will both kill anything hiding in the food and expand your food's shelf life.

There are a few options you can choose from, and it's worth familiarizing yourself with all of them. The options you have are dry ice, oxygen absorbers, diatomaceous earth, and desiccants or silica gel.

Dry Ice

Sometimes, the best treatment to rid your food of any bugs is to use dry ice. This is frozen carbon dioxide, which, as it thaws out, will displace oxygen because it is heavier. This means that when you fill up a bucket with carbon dioxide, it will remain there, as it is heavier than the surrounding air. So if you want to remove oxygen from a large container environment, such as in a 5-gallon bucket, dry ice is highly effective. It is particularly recommended if you choose to store grains and legumes in any large plastic buckets.

To treat your bucket, you will need an ounce of dry ice for every gallon. In a 5-gallon bucket, 4 ounces should suffice. Clean off any ice crystals that have been collected on the dry ice. Then, wrap it in a paper towel so it won't burn any food it comes into contact with. Put the wrapped ice on the bottom of the container and pour your grains or beans on top of it. There should be an inch of leeway at the top of the container. Attach the lid, only sealing half of it, so that the carbon dioxide can escape as the ice sublimates from the solid into gas form. This will usually take around an hour. Seal the bucket once you're sure the ice has sublimated completely. At that point, wait and see if the lid has bulged at all. If it does, release the pressure by opening the lid. Your lid should pull downward slightly to show a partial vacuum effect, and this is how you will know you've done your job properly. As the carbon dioxide is absorbed into the food, it pulls the lid down.

Oxygen Absorbers

Oxygen absorbers are usually quite effective at removing oxygen from containers, allowing them to kill insects in adult or larval form. Oxygen absorber pouches are small packets of iron powder. Oxygen and moisture can enter the packet, but the iron powder cannot leak out. The moisture in the food causes the iron to rust, and during the oxidation process, it absorbs the oxygen as well. These are highly recommended, and often more effective than vacuum packaging.

However, keep in mind that botulism may grow in high-moisture and low-oxygen environments, so make sure you only use these for low-moisture products. Use them in containers with sufficient moisture and oxygen barriers, like #10 cans, Mylar pouches, and glass canning jars. Avoid using oxygen absorbers with:

- Brown rice
- Dehydrated fruits and vegetables that won't snap when bent
- Dried eggs
- Granola
- Jerky
- Leavening agents (they may explode)
- Milled grains
- Nuts
- Pearl barley
- Salt and sugar (they turn hard with an oxygen absorber)

Different-sized containers will need different amounts of oxygen absorbers. As a general rule, use the following guidelines:

- Use 100 cc for quarts or smaller
- Use 400 cc absorbers for between a quart and a gallon
- Use 400 ccs per gallon for containers between 1 and 5 gallons

- Use a 3,000 cc for 5- and 6-gallon buckets

These guidelines err on the side of a little too much rather than not enough, because using a little extra won't do anything to your food, but not using enough is going to allow pests or bacteria to develop, or will pose a risk to the nutrition content of your food.

To use oxygen absorbers, follow these steps:

1. Prepare the containers and ensure they're entirely dry with the lid nearby.
2. Prepare the food, making sure it's free from debris, and place it in the containers.
3. Place the oxygen absorbers in a tightly closed mason jar while you're not using them. Open the jar and pull out as much as you need. Make sure it feels soft and powdery. If it feels hard or chunky, it will not absorb any more. It should also feel warm to the touch: They are warm when they're absorbing oxygen.
4. Seal the container rapidly as soon the oxygen absorber is inside.
5. Label with the date of packaging, and wait a few days or a week. Keep in mind that they absorb oxygen and not air, so it won't look fully vacuum-sealed, but it should look smaller. If it doesn't look smaller, open it up and add more, repeating the process.

Diatomaceous Earth

Diatomaceous earth is created from the fossilized remains of marine diatoms. These microscopic remains have sharp spines all over them, which can cut into insects with exoskeletons. These wounds allow for moisture to be lost from the insect, and the insects then die. People and animals typically are not negatively affected by it. However, to ensure your safety, you must make sure that you've chosen a food-grade option, rather than the kind used in swimming pool filters. You can usually find it in garden centers, hardware stores, or feed stores without too much issue.

This product is best used by taking 1 cup of diatomaceous earth to mix thoroughly into 40 pounds of grain, grain products, or legumes. Be mindful that this option is only effective against adult insects, so you still want to be as safe as possible to prevent infestation. Also keep in mind that diatomaceous earth is a dust, so it would be wise to use a mask and avoid breathing it in during the mixing process to avoid irritating your lungs.

Desiccant / Silica Gel

Desiccant will remove the moisture in the surrounding air, allowing you to create a low-moisture environment. It removes humidity to prevent the development of rust, mold, mildew, fungus, corrosion, or oxidation. It is regularly used both in food storage and in manufactured products.

Commonly, you'll find silica gel packaged in Tyvek, which meets the FDA requirement as a safe option for dry food packing. You can layer several packets throughout the container, and seal up the container immediately after. Make sure you discard the packets as soon as you open the container.

Some options may be rechargeable, so to speak, if you expose them to heat to allow them to release oxygen, but make sure you don't do this without verifying whether the type you have works this way. Silica gel is inedible, so ensure that you don't spill the packets in your food. Place them in the bottom of the container, or buried deep within its contents. Avoid placing them next to an oxygen absorber as it will interfere with its activity.

Storeroom Conditions

To wrap up this chapter, let's focus on your storeroom, which must be kept in good condition. Your storeroom needs to meet a few key criteria for better effectiveness. Remember all the different elements that you need to protect your food from? You must take the time to ensure that your storeroom is suitable for those not accounted for by your packaging.

The best packaging in the world will be useless if you've got a storeroom full of rats who will chew right through it for a quick snack. Likewise, somewhere with constant temperature fluctuations is likely to be problematic. If you want your storeroom to be effective, make sure you implement the following:

- Make sure your storeroom is cool, dry, and well-ventilated.
- Keep the temperature between 50° and 70°F.
- Keep the space free from uninsulated pipes, water heaters, or anything else that may generate heat.
- Keep the humidity level at 15% or less.
- Avoid food being kept in direct sunlight to prevent a reduction in fat-soluble vitamins.
- Store foods at least 6 inches off the floor, and 18 inches from outside walls.

The most important thing that you can do with your stockpile of food is to ensure that it is stored well. It will taste better as a result, and it will also preserve its nutritional value. When your food is stored well, it lasts significantly longer, as you will protect it from light, oxygen, insects, and rodents. By treating your food, storing it in the right containers, and keeping your storeroom in the right condition, you'll find that your food stockpile is kept better.

Chapter Summary

In this chapter, we emphasized the importance of having the right containers and treatment methods to protect your dry goods.

- The most important elements your containers need to protect against are oxygen, light, insects and rodents.
- The most popular storage options are Mylar bags, cans, PET bottles, plastic buckets, and glass jars.
- By treating with dry ice, oxygen absorbers, diatomaceous earth, or silica gel, the shelf life of foods can be extended.
- Keeping your storeroom in excellent condition is essential to ensuring that your food is kept safe.

6

CANNING 101: THE BASICS OF PRESERVING FRESH INGREDIENTS FOR MAXIMUM NUTRITIONAL VALUE

So far, we've spent a lot of time talking about dried goods, but those will only go so far, especially if you're interested in keeping fresh vegetables from your garden. This is where canning comes into play. While tins can keep dry foods long-term, you can also use canning jars if you want to preserve your produce to last in the middle of winter. With canning, you can preserve that delicious tomato sauce you made with freshly picked tomatoes, or the nutritious soup you made from scratch. Having some fruits and vegetables on hand is a great way to stretch your harvest so you're feeding yourself all year-round instead of just during the summer months.

Canning is a great way to preserve produce without damaging its nutritional content. When you choose to can your food, you usually have two options: canning with boiling water baths or canning with pressure canning. Most will be canned with pressure, but when you have high-acid foods, such as an abundance of tomatoes from your garden, you can use the boiling water bath option instead.

It might seem intimidating, but it is how people stored their food for generations before the popularization of grocery stores. You've probably heard horror stories about food poisoning, botulism, spoilage, and pressure canners blowing up, but keep in mind that if you do things just right, you'll be just fine.

You can grow your food during the summer, and then enjoy working on storing it as it's harvested. By reading this chapter, you'll discover what you need to know about canning to make sure you're doing it safely. We'll begin by discussing the vegetables that don't usually can very well, followed by how canning works. We'll go over the tools and then the process itself. We'll break it down into a few simple steps: sterilizing jars, filling jars, and then canning. We will discuss both the boiling water bath and the pressure canning methods. Finally, we'll go over the processing time for the most common produce people tend to can.

VEGETABLES THAT DON'T CAN WELL

Some produce simply doesn't can well. It may pose a risk to your health if you can it, or it may taste so bad you won't want to bother. Many of these items fare much better if you freeze them instead.

Broccoli

Broccoli isn't necessarily dangerous to can, but it won't taste very good when you open it up. It will be so mushy and soft that it won't be enjoyable. It's usually better to pickle it if you want to store it, or you can choose to freeze your broccoli instead.

Brussels Sprouts

Brussels sprouts are unappealing when canned as they get slimy and lose their flavor. They usually do well when they're pickled, however, so they can still be preserved.

Cabbage

Cabbage will be safe to eat after pressure canning it, but it will be slimy, mushy and unenjoyable. However, pickling it is a good option.

Cauliflower

Like broccoli, cauliflower will not be harmful to eat, but it won't be enjoyable when it's been canned. Pressure canning is likely to create something mushy and unpleasant to eat.

Celery

Celery does not currently have an approved method of canning. Some people will attempt it anyway, but it's not been safety-tested, so there are no safe processing times currently determined. If you want to save celery, freeze it instead.

Eggplant

Eggplant will become mushy and ultimately disgusting if you use a pressure canner. However, you can pickle it if you want to.

Kohlrabi

Canned kohlrabi usually has unpleasant and overly soft results. It's better to pickle this vegetable instead of trying to save it. You can choose to freeze it instead.

Lettuce

Like cabbage, lettuce will become slimy and inedible if it is canned. Lettuce is not heated to eat, and it also doesn't freeze well. There is no good way to store it long-term. Stick to enjoying your lettuce fresh.

Zucchini

There has not yet been any research into how to can zucchini properly. Because squash, like zucchini, is a little bit acidic, it is at risk of developing botulism in low-oxygen environments, and currently, it is unknown how long zucchini should be processed in a pressure canner. Rather than pressure canning it, consider pickling it or freezing it instead.

HOW CANNING WORKS

Canning, despite sounding intimidating, is simple. It works by putting foods in jars or other similar, heat-tolerant containers such as cans, and heating them to temperatures that will destroy all the potential microorganisms that may have been present in the food to cause it to spoil. As the jar is heated, the air is forced out from the jar, and when it cools off again, a vacuum seal is created. This vacuum seal then prevents any air from re-entering the jar, which locks out any microorganisms that could have contaminated it.

Usually, the jar is heated in one of two ways. You can use a boiling-water bath, which is usually recommended for fruits, tomatoes, jellies and jams, pickles, and other pickled goods. In the bath, jars are heated by covering them completely with boiling water to cook for a specified amount of time. I've included a handy chart at the end of this chapter for you to use as a reference to see how long each food you'd like to can will need to be warmed.

You can also use pressure canning, which is currently the only safe method you can use to preserve vegetables, meats, seafood, or poultry. During pressure canning, the jars are placed in a few inches of water within a pressure cooker, which is then heated to at least 240°F. This is achieved through pressurizing the environment. This method is necessary because of clostridium botulinum. This is the organism responsible for botulism. Though the cells can be killed at boiling temperatures, the spores they create can still survive. The spores can grow rapidly in low-acid foods, which meats and veggies are classed as. As the spores grow, they then release toxins that can be deadly. These spores are only killed off when you pressure-cook food at a temperature of 240°F or higher for a specific amount of time, depending upon the type of food and your altitude.

High-acid foods can usually kill the spores without allowing for the release of the toxins, but to reach that acidity, the food would need to have a pH of 4.6 or lower. This is typically applicable to fruits or pickled vegetables which are canned in brine or vinegar. Some foods, like tomatoes, are close to this pH value, so they are usually canned with the addition of some lemon juice or citric acid.

WHAT YOU NEED FOR CANNING

Food safety is no joke, and it's so easy to unintentionally set up an environment to become infected with botulism. You need to make sure you have the right tools on hand. While it's highly unlikely that, even if you can something poorly, it will develop botulism, the risk is there, and it's always better to be safe than sorry, especially where your family's wellbeing is concerned. The best thing you can do when it comes to canning is to ensure that you gather all the right tools to help protect the foods.

Canning Jars and Lids

Canning jars come in several shapes and sizes, with many different lids. Ultimately, the ones you choose are up to you. So long as they are glass and well-made, they're good enough to use. Just make sure that none of them are damaged before you get started.

You'll also want to make sure that you have the right lids. Some jars are reusable, but others must be replaced each time you use them. Verify which kind you have, and when in doubt, always opt for new lids if you're unsure. Select jars in various sizes so you can store everything from jams to sauces and larger quantities of veggies or pickles. Lids may be one-piece or two-piece, so long as you verify that they're the right size.

Tongs or Jar Remover

Tongs may work just fine for removing jars, but you run the risk dropping them, which could be dangerous at such high temperatures. It's recommended that you get a jar remover, which has rubber grips that won't conduct heat, and will grip the top of your jar tightly as you remove it from the water bath.

Funnel

A canning funnel is specifically designed to fit into jars to allow you to keep your rims cleaner, which is necessary in order to get a proper seal. They also allow you to get everything into the jar easily, since you'll be able to use the funnel to guide everything in. Choose one specifically designed for filling jars for the best results.

A Pressure Canner

Canning can be done in just about any large pot, but if you're going to pressure can, you'll need something that will create the necessary pressure. A pressure canner will trap the steam within it to pressurize the container and raise the temperature further.

THE CANNING PROCESS

Sterilizing Jars

The first step of canning is to begin the process with sterile jars. This is essential. While the process of canning will raise the temperature to kill bacteria, it's still good to make sure you're working with as clean an environment as possible: If you're off with your temperatures even a little, you'll be risking a lot. The sterilization process is, thankfully, quite easy.

- **Discard damaged jars.** Start by going through all the jars you intend to use and inspecting them carefully. Any cracks or nicks in the jar's rim can interfere with the vacuum seal you're trying to achieve. If you notice any jars that are damaged, discard them. They're not safe to use.
- **Sanitize jars and lids.** When you know which cans you'll be using, wash them in hot water with soap, and dry them completely. Alternatively, you can run them through the dishwasher to sanitize them and get them ready to go.
- **Keep jars warm.** Once they've been sanitized, set your jars in the oven, set at 180ºF. This is an essential step: You don't want to put hot food into

a cold jar, or a cold jar into a boiling hot bath. By keeping them hot, you can prevent this from happening.

Filling Jars

With the jars prepared and ready to fill, it's time to load them up. Keep in mind that all the jars are still hot, so do not handle them bare-handed. Instead, use a jar lifter or oven mitts to protect yourself. With that in mind, take the following steps to fill the jars:

- **Fill Jars:** Using your funnel, pour food or liquid into the jars. Each recipe you choose to jar will have a different allowance for headspace, which will vary by ingredients. Follow this recommendation. The headspace is the space in the jar between the food and the top of the jar.
- **Remove Air Bubbles:** When the jars are full, use something long and skinny, like a wooden skewer or rubber spatula, to dislodge any air bubbles. There are bubble remover tools, but these are rarely necessary.
- **Wipe Rims:** When all the jars are filled, make sure the rims are clean to prevent anything from impeding a vacuum seal. Now's not the time to be messy: You want everything as immaculate as possible. You can use a clean, damp cloth for this process. Just make sure there's no lint left behind.

- **Tighten Lids:** Place the lids on the jars and tighten them. If you're using two-piece jar lids, make sure you center the flat part and then tighten the band until it is finger-tight. Your jars are now ready for processing.

Boiling Water Bath

The boiling water bath method is quite easy. When your jars are ready to be processed, you can simply move on. Remember that you should only use the boiling water bath if you're canning something high in acid. This can't be reiterated enough. Any low-acid foods should *never* be processed in this manner. It's repeated as often as it is for a reason: Botulism is fatal, sometimes up to 50% of the time, if you cannot seek medical treatment. Don't risk it. Properly can your food.

High-acid foods can be stored for between 12 and 18 months in this manner, so if you want to preserve your fruits or acidic vegetables using this method, continue with the rest of these instructions. Otherwise, skip to the next section to learn how to pressure can.

How to Boil Jars

When it's time to boil your jars, there are a few simple steps, and the only extra equipment you'll need is a container that is deep enough to allow for the jars to be submerged, and something that will lift the jars off the bottom of the pot to allow for full circulation of the water as they are boiled. There are many jar-lifters you can get for this process.

1. Make sure that your jars have been sterilized before you begin the canning process. Once you have sterilized jars, place them in a large pot and fill the pot with water. The water needs to be able to cover the jars. Begin to simmer the water at 180°F for 10 minutes. This is done to prevent the jars from breaking when they are filled with hot food (this process is called hot packing) or when the jars are placed in the boiling water bath. It is important to keep the jars in the simmering water until they are ready to be hot-packed.

2. Using a funnel, fill the food into the hot jars. Refer to the recipe or table you are using to gauge the required headspace (the empty space that needs to be left between the food and the lid). It is important to remove any air bubbles that may have been created, so taking a non-metal tool like a spatula or a plastic chopstick, carefully work the tool down the jars and remove any air bubbles. You might need to put more food into the jar to maintain the headspace once the air bubbles have been removed.

3. Clean off any leftover sauce on the jar rims. This can be done with a cloth or damp paper towel. This will ensure the jars are sealed properly.

4. Next, place the bands and lids on the jars. Tighten

the bands until you feel slight resistance. Make sure not to overtighten the jars. It will not make the jars seal better in fact you will achieve the opposite. Always use new lids. You can reuse bands if they are in good condition

5. Fill the canner halfway with boiling water. Bring the water to a full simmer. Gently lower the jars one at a time into the water with a jar lifter. You can use a canning rack to lower all the jars at once, but being gentle is the key. Pay close attention to the water level. If the water level does not cover the jars by 1 to 2 inches, you will need to add more boiling water until the water covers the jars. Bring the water to a rolling boil, cover the canner and boil for as long as the recipe requires.

6. Once the time is up, turn off the heat, remove the lid and let the water in the canner cool for 10 minutes before you take the jars out.

7. Use the jar lifter to remove the jars and let them cool. Keeping them upright on a towel, wire rack, or cutting board, keep them roughly 1 to 2 inches apart. Do not retighten the rims even if you hear a pinging noise. This is just the jars cooling and sealing. Leave the jars in their new position without any disturbances for 12-24 hours.

8. Checking the seals is an exciting and important part of the canning process. Simply push the center of the lid down. You are looking for the center of the lid to remain down and not pop up.

To double-check the seal, remove the band and try to remove the lid. If the lid does not move, you have a good seal. Sadly, if the center does pop up or you are able to remove the lid easily, the jar is not sealed. In this case, store the food in the fridge for up to 3 weeks or in the freezer for up to 1 year.

9. Label all jars and store them in a cool, dark, and dry place, so they are ready to enjoy!

Pressure Canning

For your low-acid foods, pressure canning will keep them safe. This is also effective if you want to can complete meals, like soups, stews and sauces. You can even preserve meats in this fashion if you want something shelf-stable. This process will require you to get a pressure canner.

How to Pressure Can

This process is a bit more involved than using a water bath, but it can be just as effective. You will want to follow these steps:

1. Begin with sterilized jars and lids. Then place a rack in the bottom of your pressure canner. Add boiling water to it. Usually, you want to have about 3 inches of water at the bottom of the canner.
2. Place your filled jars into the canner, not touching anywhere, then attach the lid. Allow the steam to leave the petcock opening for 10 minutes, then shut it until the steam comes out in a steady stream.
3. Turn the heat off, and leave the whole thing alone until the pressure has reached 0 and stays there for a few minutes. Then, you can remove the lid and start pulling out the jars with the jar lifter. Leave them to cool completely on a dry tea towel.

Processing Time

Boiling Method (Acidic Foods)

Headspace: On all high acid foods listed in the tables below leave 1/2 inch headspace. With the exception of

strawberry jam which needs 1/4 inch and grapes which
need 1 inch headspace.

FOOD TYPE	PACK METHOD	PROCESS TIME (PINT)	PROCESS TIME (QUART)
APPLES	HOT	20 MINS	20 MINS
APRICOTS	RAW; HOT	25 MINS; 20 MINS	30 MINS; 25 MINS
BLACKBERRIES	RAW; HOT	15 MINS; 15 MINS	20 MINS; 15 MINS
BLUEBERRIES	RAW; HOT	15 MINS; 15 MINS	20 MINS; 15 MINS
CRANBERRIES	HOT	15 MINS	15 MINS
CHERRIES	RAW; HOT	25 MINS; 15 MINS	30 MINS; 20 MINS
CUCUMBERS (PICKLED)	RAW	10 MINS	15 MINS
GRAPEFRUIT	RAW	10 MINS	15 MINS
GRAPES	RAW; HOT	15 MINS; 10 MINS	20 MINS; 10 MINS

FOOD TYPE	PACK METHOD	PROCESS TIME (PINT)	PROCESS TIME (QUART)
NECTARINES	RAW; HOT	25 MINS; 20 MINS	30 MINS; 25 MINS
ORANGES	RAW	10 MINS	10 MINS
PEACHES	RAW; HOT	25 MINS; 20 MINS	30 MINS; 25 MINS
PEARS	RAW; HOT	25 MINS; 20 MINS	30 MINS; 25 MINS
PINEAPPLE	HOT	15 MINS	20 MINS
PLUMS	RAW; HOT	20 MINS; 25 MINS	20 MINS; 25 MINS
RASPBERRIES	RAW; HOT	15 MINS; 15 MINS	20 MINS; 15 MINS
RHUBARB	HOT	15 MINS	15 MINS
STRAWBERRY JAM	HOT	5 MINS	15 MINS

FOOD TYPE	PACK METHOD	PROCESS TIME (PINT)	PROCESS TIME (QUART)
TOMATO JUICE	HOT	35 MINS	40 MINS
TOMATOES (WHOLE, HALVED)	RAW	85 MINS	85 MINS
TOMATOES (CRUSHED)	HOT	35 MINS	40 MINS

THE PROCESSING TIMES FOR THE COMPLETE TABLES ABOVE ARE FOR CANNING AT SEA LEVEL. MODIFY AS SHOWN IN THE TABLE BELOW:

PROCESSING TIME AT SEA LEVEL	MODIFIED PROCESSING TIME
20 MINUTES OR LESS	ADD 1 MINUTE PER 1000 FT. IN ELEVATION
OVER 20 MINUTES	ADD 2 MINUTES PER 1000 FT. IN ELEVATION

* * *

Pressure Canning (Acidic Foods)

Headspace: On all high acidic foods listed below leave 1/2 inch headspace. For each 1000 feet above sea level increase the headspace by 1/8 inch. For pint jars do not exceed 1 inch headspace and on quart jars 1 3/4 inch headspace.

FOOD TYPE	PACK METHOD	PROCESS TIME PINT	PROCESS TIME QUART	PSI UNDER 2,000 FT.	PSI 2,001-4,000 FT.	PSI 4,001-6,000 FT.	PSI 6,001-8,000 FT.
APPLES	HOT	8 MINS	8 MINS	6 LB	7 LB	8 LB	9 LB
APRICOTS	RAW; HOT	10 MINS; 10 MINS	10 MINS; 10 MINS	6 LB; 6 LB	7 LB; 7 LB	8 LB; 8 LB	9 LB; 9 LB
BLACKBERRIES	RAW; HOT	8 MINS; 8 MINS	10 MINS; 8 MINS	6 LB; 6 LB	7 LB; 7 LB	8 LB; 8 LB	9 LB; 9 LB
BLUEBERRIES	RAW; HOT	8 MINS; 8 MINS	10 MINS; 8 MINS	6 LB; 6 LB	7 LB; 7 LB	8 LB; 8 LB	9 LB; 9 LB
CHERRIES	RAW; HOT	10 MINS; 8 MINS	10 MINS; 10 MINS	6 LB; 6 LB	7 LB; 7 LB	8 LB; 8 LB	9 LB; 9 LB
GRAPEFRUIT	RAW; HOT	8 MINS; 10 MINS	10 MINS; 10 MINS	6 LB; 6 LB	7 LB; 7 LB	8 LB; 8 LB	9 LB; 9 LB
NECTARINES	RAW; HOT	10 MINS; 10 MINS	10 MINS; 10 MINS	6 LB; 6 LB	7 LB; 7 LB	8 LB; 8 LB	9 LB; 9 LB
ORANGES	RAW; HOT	8 MINS; 10 MINS	10 MINS; 10 MINS	6 LB; 6 LB	7 LB; 7 LB	8 LB; 8 LB	9 LB; 9 LB
PEACHES	RAW; HOT	10 MINS; 10 MINS	10 MINS; 10 MINS	6 LB; 6 LB	7 LB; 7 LB	8 LB; 8 LB	9 LB; 9 LB
PEARS	HOT	10 MINS	10 MINS	6 LB	7 LB	8 LB	9 LB

FOOD TYPE	PACK METHOD	PROCESS TIME PINT	PROCESS TIME QUART	PSI UNDER 2,000 FT.	PSI 2,001- 4,000 FT.	PSI 4,001- 6,000 FT.	PSI 6,001- 8,000 FT.
PLUMS	RAW; HOT	10 MINS; 10 MINS	10 MINS; 10 MINS	6 LB; 6 LB	7 LB; 7 LB	8 LB; 8 LB	9 LB; 9 LB
RASPBERRIES	RAW; HOT	8 MINS; 10 MINS	10 MINS; 8 MINS	6 LB; 6 LB	7 LB; 7 LB	8 LB; 8 LB	9 LB; 9 LB
RHUBARB	HOT	8 MINS	8 MINS	6 LB	7 LB	8 LB	9 LB
TOMATO JUICE	HOT	20 MINS	20 MINS	6 LB	7 LB	8 LB	9 LB
TOMATOES (WHOLE, HALVED)	RAW	40 MINS	40 MINS	6 LB	7 LB	8 LB	9 LB
TOMATOES (CRUSHED)	HOT	20 MINS	20 MINS	6 LB	7 LB	8 LB	9 LB

* * *

Pressure Canning (Low Acid Foods)

Headspace: On all low acid foods listed below leave 1 inch headspace. Except lima beans, raw packed in quart size jars, increase headspace to 1 1/2 inch for small beans and for large beans 1 1/4 inch. For each 1000 feet above sea level increase the headspace by 1/8 inch. For pint jars do not exceed 1 inch headspace and on quart jars 1 3/4 inch headspace.

FOOD TYPE	PACK METHOD	PROCESS TIME PINT	PROCESS TIME QUART	PSI UNDER 2,000 FT.	PSI 2,001-4,000 FT.	PSI 4,001-6,000 FT.	PSI 6,001-8,000 FT.
ARTICHOKES (JERUSALEM)	HOT	25 MINS	25 MINS	11 LB	12 LB	13 LB	14 LB
ASPARAGUS	RAW; HOT	30 MINS; 30 MINS	40 MINS; 40 MINS	11 LB; 11 LB	12 LB; 12 LB	13 LB; 13 LB	14 LB; 14 LB
BEANS (GREEN OR YELLOW)	RAW; HOT	20 MINS; 20 MINS	25 MINS; 25 MINS	11 LB; 11 LB	12 LB; 12 LB	13 LB; 13 LB	14 LB; 14 LB
BEETS	HOT	30 MINS	35 MINS	11 LB	12 LB	13 LB	14 LB
CARROTS	RAW; HOT	25 MINS; 25 MINS	30 MINS; 30 MINS	11 LB; 11 LB	12 LB; 12 LB	13 LB; 13 LB	14 LB; 14 LB
CORN	RAW; HOT	55 MINS; 55 MINS	85 MINS; 85 MINS	11 LB; 11 LB	12 LB; 12 LB	13 LB; 13 LB	14 LB; 14 LB
LIMA BEANS	RAW; HOT	40 MINS; 40 MINS	50 MINS; 50 MINS	11 LB; 11 LB	12 LB; 12 LB	13 LB; 13 LB	14 LB; 14 LB
MUSHROOMS	HOT	45 MINS	---	11 LB	12 LB	13 LB	14 LB
OKRA	RAW; HOT	25 MINS; 25 MINS	40 MINS; 40 MINS	11 LB; 11 LB	12 LB; 12 LB	13 LB; 13 LB	14 LB; 14 LB
PEAS	RAW; HOT	40 MINS; 40 MINS	40 MINS; 40 MINS	11 LB; 11 LB	12 LB; 12 LB	13 LB; 13 LB	14 LB; 14 LB
PEPPERS	HOT	35 MINS	---	11 LB	12 LB	13 LB	14 LB

FOOD TYPE	PACK METHOD	PROCESS TIME PINT	PROCESS TIME QUART	PSI UNDER 2,000 FT.	PSI 2,001-4,000 FT.	PSI 4,001-6,000 FT.	PSI 6,001-8,000 FT.
POTATOES (WHITE)	HOT	35 MINS	40 MINS	11 LB	12 LB	13 LB	14 LB
PUMPKIN	HOT	55 MINS	90 MINS	11 LB	12 LB	13 LB	14 LB
SPINACH AND LEAFY GREENS	HOT	70 MINS	90 MINS	11 LB	12 LB	13 LB	14 LB
WINTER SQUASH	HOT	55 MINS	90 MINS	11 LB	12 LB	13 LB	14 LB
SWEET POTATOES	HOT	65 MINS	90 MINS	11 LB	12 LB	13 LB	14 LB

* * *

Canning foods is a great way for you to keep them for longer than they'd otherwise last in the fridge or on a shelf. However, it can also cause changes to the texture of your food. As you know by now, certain foods simply don't can well, but they can be pickled. When you can your food, you must make sure that you do so in the right way. While all foods can be pressure canned, not all canning-friendly foods can be canned with a bath. Remember that because of the risk of botulism, foods should always be canned according to the recommendations for those foods.

Chapter Summary

In this chapter, we have reviewed how to can fresh foods so they can be kept on a shelf. We covered:

- What canning will do and how it keeps your food safe.
- Which foods shouldn't be canned.
- What you need in order to can your food.
- How to sterilize and fill jars.
- How to use a boiling water bath.
- How to use a pressure canner.
- Why it's so important to pressure can low-acid foods.
- The processing times for varying foods.

7

THE CHEST FREEZER: WHY YOU NEED ONE NOW, AND WHAT YOU NEED TO FILL IT WITH

Your stockpile isn't complete without a chest freezer that's been loaded up with fresh ingredients to thaw and use later. Most emergencies aren't likely to completely disrupt your ability to access power, so it's always a good idea to keep frozen food on hand. Plus, you can usually take advantage of some great shopping deals when you have a chest freezer, whether that's through catching meat on sale at a great price or taking advantage of the hunting season.

A chest freezer will provide you with extra space. For many people, the freezer attached to their refrigerator is a great start, but there's a good chance that you can't keep much more than a few days' worth of meat in there, especially if you're already keeping frozen snacks, convenience meals, and ice cream in there. A deep freezer can become a sort of reserve area where you can store meat for longer periods. They're also good for storing bread, vegetables, fruits for smoothies, eggs, and prepared foods that are quick and easy to heat.

This is likely to be your first line of defense if you can't easily get to the grocery store, as the food usually tastes better than canned food, it's more nutritious, and it's likely to be closer to what you normally eat. However, it's a good idea to make sure you don't only stock up in this manner, as if something happens to the power, you'll lose everything in a few days.

If you want to be on the safe side, you should consider an alternative source of electricity in case the grid were to go down for an extended period of time.

As you read through this chapter, we'll go over why a chest freezer is better than an upright model. We'll discuss the benefits of freezing foods and why it's so widely recommended. We'll discuss what to prioritize when your freezer space is limited, and what should be left out of the freezer entirely. We'll also go over some simple tips that you can use to ensure that you're able to maximize the use of your freezer and keep your family fed and happy, even in an emergency.

WHY CHOOSE A CHEST FREEZER?

Chest freezers aren't always the most popular choice. They have a much larger footprint than an upright freezer, and it's often harder to dig through them to find what you're looking for just because many foodstuffs will wind up buried as you fill up the freezer. You can only see what's on the top layer, which, while inconvenient, can be a good thing, as we'll be discussing.

While a chest freezer is undoubtedly less convenient, it's the better option if you're choosing to stockpile food, and there are several reasons for this. If you have the option, it's always better for you to select a chest freezer over other models.

More Usable Space

Chest freezers may not be fun to dig through, but you can benefit from more usable space. There is roughly 20% more usable space in a chest freezer than in a similarly-sized upright freezer. That increase in usable space means 20% more food you can stash away for when you need it.

More Consistent Temperature

Chest freezers keep a more consistent temperature than upright models. This is because they don't come with a self-defrost system. This is good for your food: It's more likely to stay safely frozen rather than thawing out. However, it may need to be defrosted now and then when frost has accumulated.

Less Air Circulation

Chest freezers don't have as much space for air circulation. This is a great thing for the long-term storage of food: Your food is going to be well-protected from freezer burn.

Keeps Food Frozen Longer

If there is a blackout or something that causes you to lose all power for an extended period, a chest freezer will keep your food frozen for longer just because you can fill up so much more space. The proximity of other frozen items will help each one stay frozen for longer.

Uses Less Electricity

Most chest freezers use up less electricity than uprights, but you'll have to compare while you're shopping to make sure you select the most energy-efficient option.

WHY FREEZE YOUR FOOD

You might wonder if there are any inherent benefits to freezing your food, and in fact, there are many. Freezing food is a fantastic way to save on food, and many people who garden and hunt go out of their way to have several chest freezers on hand so that they're able to keep all of their bounties from going bad.

Freezing your food is highly effective for keeping it safe. If you keep the temperature at a constant 32°F, then the food is going to be safe, whether it's one year or four years old. Will it taste as good? Probably not. Usually, long-term storage can affect the taste a little.

Ideally, you want to get a good deep freezer; the lower the temperature you can get from your freezer, the better. Typically, the foods at the bottom of your freezer will fare better than the foods at the top, where they may be exposed to regular temperatures during the day.

By freezing food, you'll get the added benefit of enjoying fresh meat, fish, bread, and other complete meals that have already been prepared. This allows for better nutrition and variety, and you can even tailor your meals to what you want to eat each day. If you're sick, you could prioritize pulling out the ingredients to make a fresh, nutritious soup, for example. This isn't possible with canned foods. You'll also get better taste and texture out of your frozen food as it wasn't cooked during the canning process and then left to sit in its moisture for an extended amount of time. It will taste truer to its original state, especially if you can keep the food minimally processed and well frozen.

WHAT TO PRIORITIZE WHEN FREEZER SPACE IS LIMITED

When you've got limited space in your freezer, it's tough to figure out which foods you want to store. However, some foods are better to keep than others. Generally, you'll want to keep foods that don't take up as much space. You may even want to make it a point to break down certain items so they fit better in the limited space you have. For example, imagine you have a whole chicken you just bought from the store. It's going to take up a lot more space than if you take the time to spatchcock it or to butcher it entirely.

You want to prioritize proteins like meat, poultry, and fish. These are usually better frozen than canned, but you can them if you'd like to. Then, prioritize any fruits and vegetables that don't suit the canning process. From there, you can add additional vegetables and fruits if you prefer them to be in a whole or frozen state. They could be great for smoothies. If you've already stocked up on these, you can store breads, baked goods, and leftovers from meals. Just keep in mind that some things may change in flavor or texture during the freezing process.

What Not to Freeze

Just as some foods aren't suitable for canning, several foods may not do so well frozen. Generally, the more processed something is, the worse it will fare in freezing. You want to avoid freezing products such as:

- Bacon
- Canned meats or fish
- Cream cheese
- Deli meats and cheeses
- Eggplant
- Melon
- Raw potatoes
- Radishes
- Salads and lettuce
- Sprouts
- Whole eggs (they may freeze decently if cracked and stored, or if you scramble and cook them first, but there will be a change in texture)

FREEZING TIPS

When freezing food for storage, there are ways you can help extend the time that it will remain undamaged by freezer burn. There are also ways that you can keep track of your stash better, so you always know exactly what you have available to you. By following the tips and tricks provided here, you can protect your food from freezer burn, fit more into your storage, and ensure that, in the event of a power outage, your food will remain safe in the time before the power comes back on.

Leave No Space Unfilled

By filling every space of your freezer, you can achieve two goals. First, it is harder for your freezer to warm up when there is more in there, meaning that in the event of a power outage, the food won't thaw out as quickly. The food in the freezer will act like ice packs to help insulate all the other food in there. Second, by filling every space efficiently, you can fit more into your freezer, extending your stash and ensuring that you'll have more available to you when you need it.

If there are sizeable gaps in your freezer and you're not quite ready to fill them in with food, consider adding in jugs or bags full of water. These will fill in space to protect your food, and you can simply pull them out when it's time to put more food in its place.

However, keep in mind that you shouldn't pack food too tightly either, as water expands when it freezes. To prevent damage to the food or the storage bags, keeping the right amount of food is essential.

Cool Completely before Freezing

While it might seem like common sense to cool food before putting it into a freezer, this is something that some people will forego, especially if they're trying to put away precooked meals. However, by putting in foods that aren't already cooled, you are causing the freezer's temperature to rise. It may not be enough to thaw out your food, but it is a health hazard. You can thaw and refreeze certain foods without realizing it, which can dramatically reduce the shelf-life of the food. Always make sure that food is at least at room temperature, but preferably cooler, before putting it into your freezer.

Label and Date Everything

When you don't label your foods, you may thaw something entirely different from what you were expecting. That frozen beef stew? It might end up being soup or a sauce from a pre-made meal. A chunk of what you think is ham may end up being some pork loin. By labeling everything, you will know exactly what's in each bag: no surprises. If applicable, the label should also include preparation instructions.

Dating everything is essential as well. While, technically, food may remain safe indefinitely when you leave it in a freezer, it will not remain tasty indefinitely. It will lose quality over time, so you will want to use older foods first. This means you need a dating system so you can compare which food is newer before selecting it.

Seal Properly

Before putting any food into the freezer, a proper seal is essential if you want to extend the longevity of the food.

You don't want frost to enter and change the taste of the foods.

Use a Vacuum Sealer for Long-Term Storage

This brings us to our next tip: using vacuum sealers for long-term storage. These can be incredibly handy items, whether you're saving dry goods or foods to put in the freezer. A vacuum sealer is relatively inexpensive and you can use it to ensure that all the air has been pulled out of the storage bag. By getting that perfect seal with no air coming through, the food is protected better and for longer. You can extend how long food lasts in the freezer once it's been vacuum-sealed.

Keep the Freezer Frost-Free

Freezers shouldn't be full of frost when you open them up. Identifying frost in the freezer is a sign that moisture is coming into contact with coils. This can cause problems with odors, storage space being taken up by frost, and even difficulty with shutting the door. Frost may also cause freezer burn on food as moisture evaporates and freezes, ruining the taste of the food.

Freeze in Portion Sizes

If you've got a massive amount of meat or pre-made meals to freeze, it's always a good idea to freeze them in portion sizes for individuals or the entire family. This way, you are only ever defrosting what you need, rather than having to pull out an entire roasting joint when you only need half to feed everyone. Portion sizes are also a little easier to puzzle-piece together when necessary to maximize space in your freezer.

Keep Long-Term Storage on the Bottom

This may be a bit of common sense, but if you have things you're keeping long-term for any reason, these foods should go to the bottom of the freezer. The bottom is the coldest part, which means the food will keep longer, but you're also not having to dig past it constantly to access other items that you have in there.

Freezers are vital tools, but they should always be used in tandem with other methods of storing your food. This means that if you're going to keep food in a freezer to reap the higher nutritional benefits this method of storage offers, you should have plenty of canned or shelf-stable options as well. Remember that you could lose power, or your freezer could die on you. It may not happen, but it's always better to be prepared. Keep your freezer stocked with meat, fish, poultry, vegetables, and fruits, and if you have room, toss in some pre-made meals for easy access.

Chapter Summary

In this chapter, we discussed the importance of freezing food for emergency scenarios. The key points to remember are:

- Chest freezers are better than standing freezers.

- When you have limited freezer space, prioritize meat, poultry, fish, vegetables, and fruits.

- Food can be frozen indefinitely if it remains frozen, but it will lose flavor and nutrients.

- A freezer is a valuable tool, but it should not be your only line of defense.

8

DEHYDRATING 101: EVERYTHING YOU NEED TO KNOW TO PRESERVE NUTRITIONAL CONTENT THROUGH DEHYDRATION

I f you're looking for ways to store food that are not dependent on refrigeration, dehydration is a great way to do so. Dehydrated foods pack all the nutritional punch of fresh foods, without the space commitment and stringent storage parameters. Dehydrated foods that were nutritious while fresh will also be nutritious when dried. All you have to do is add some water and you'll have a meal, or at least a component of one.

In this chapter, we will discuss what dehydration is and the benefits it offers. We'll discuss the most common methods of dehydration, as well as what should not be dehydrated. Then we'll take the time to go over how to dehydrate several foods. Finally, we'll wrap it up by discussing how to rehydrate food.

Dehydration provides you with the ability to preserve the nutritional value of produce by removing all water from the food. With little moisture in the food, you'll be able to then extend the lifespan of it. Without moisture, it's difficult for most bacteria to grow on it, even if the food is not refrigerated. Dehydrated foods may remain fresh for 5–15 years.

METHODS OF DEHYDRATION

Dehydration can be achieved in several ways: air drying, sun drying, oven drying, through food dehydrators, or even in smokehouses. The method you choose is entirely based upon resources available to you, as well as your preference.

Air Drying

Air drying involves hanging foods indoors to dry in the air. There must be good airflow for this, and foods must be protected from dirt and insects. Keep in mind that this only really works in low-humidity areas, or the food may develop mold before it dries.

Sun Drying

Sun drying is the oldest method of drying. It is entirely free if you live somewhere with plenty of sun. However, because it requires the weather to be onside, it cannot be planned for accurately. Food will usually take three or four days to dry in the sun, and if it doesn't dry in that period, it's likely to develop mold. Ideally, the sky should be clear and the temperature should be 95°F or higher for three to five days, along with less than 20% humidity. If you can't guarantee all these conditions, this method is not for you.

Oven Drying

The oven can dry food easily. It may take six or more hours to dry food properly. These foods will require low heat, and some may only require a gas pilot light to dry effectively. You should set your oven to 140°F if possible, leaving the door ajar to allow for circulation. However, this is a very expensive method due to how long it will take. You may also accidentally burn food.

FOOD DEHYDRATORS

Food dehydrators contain some sort of heating element, alongside fans and vents to heat the air and circulate it to dry out foods. Dried foods will shrink and become lighter, and with a good dehydrator, more flavor and color are kept. These usually allow for more food to be dried faster, consistently, and sometimes more energy efficiently. However, these devices take up counter space, and they can be expensive if you choose one with all the bells and whistles.

Smokehouse Drying

Foods, especially meats, can be dried in a smoker. This will not only dry out the food, but it will add a nice smoky flavor as well. This usually requires a temperature of 145°–150ºF, with plenty of smoke to dry the food out.

This can take between 12 and 72 hours, depending on the food.

What Not to Dehydrate

Some foods that may be available commercially in dried forms are not safe to dry at home for safety reasons. In particular, you want to avoid dehydrating butter, cheese, eggs, or milk. It's too easy to do so poorly or cause spoilage. However, dried eggs, cheese, butter, and milk should definitely be purchased as part of your stockpile.

PREPARING FOODS FOR DEHYDRATION

The best foods to dehydrate are those that will hold their nutritional value easily. Leafy greens, many forms of produce, and some meats can be dehydrated easily for simple snacks. However, before dehydrating, certain foods must be treated first.

Blanching before Dehydration

Certain foods must be blanched before being dehydrated. This is cooking food in steam or water for a specific amount of time, and then cooling it quickly. Blanching works well for asparagus, carrots, peas, tomatoes, cranberries, cherries, onions, blueberries, plums, pears, potatoes, pumpkin, turnips, wax or green beans, and rutabagas. To blanch, you will need a stockpot of boiling water, a bowl of icy water, and a slotted spoon. Simply follow these steps:

1. Bring the water in the stockpot to a boil.
2. Add vegetables to create an even layer on top of the water. Put on the lid and let them cook according to the instructions for the food you're dehydrating.
3. After the time has elapsed, remove the food with a slotted spoon and place it in the ice bath to cool.
4. Once it's cool, drain the food and let it dry. Pat it dry if necessary. It should then be ready to dehydrate.

Boiling Before Dehydration

Certain foods benefit from a quick boil to soften them up before being dehydrated. The most common include butternut squash, beets, potatoes, corn, rhubarb, and beans.

Preparing Meat for Dehydration

Before you dehydrate meat, you must cook it. The cooking method that you choose to use is up to you.

Preparing Fruits for Dehydration

Many fruits will require a dip in citric acid or lemon juice to prevent oxidation, which will cause nutrient loss. Certain fruits, such as bananas, apples, pears, and light-colored stone fruits benefit from this treatment. To do so, you will need citric acid (lemon juice works well), a big bowl or clean sink, and a slotted spoon.

1. Prepare the pre-treatment solution. Citric acid will provide instructions for the particular concentration you need. If you use lemon juice, use one cup of juice for every quart of water, and mix it well.
2. Soak food for up to 10 minutes with lemon juice, or as directed with citric acid.
3. Remove all fruits with the slotted spoon, letting them drain. Dry with a paper towel if possible. The fruits are now ready to be dehydrated.

DEHYDRATING USING A DEHYDRATOR

What You Need

- Dehydrator
- Parchment paper
- Instructions for the ingredient (easily found online)
- Citric acid (prevents oxidation and browning of fruits)
- Storage containers (Mylar bags work well)

Instructions

1. Begin by washing and drying each piece of food. If you're not using organic foods, soak them to remove pesticides. To do this, soak fruits and vegetables in a sink filled with ½ cup baking soda and a bit of dish soap. Let them soak for 20 minutes. Then drain, rinse in cool water, and dry well.
2. Pre-treat any foods that require it. Some foods may need to be blanched, boiled, or dipped.
3. Blanching involves heating food in steam or water and then cooling quickly in an ice bath.
4. Boiling is required to soften certain foods before dehydrating.
5. Dipping involves treating food with citric acid or lemon juice to prevent oxidation.

6. Preheat the dehydrator. Most fruits and vegetables will dry at 135°F, but confirm this for each item before doing so.

7. Place food in single layers on trays. Foods that may become sticky should not touch at all. Use parchment paper liners for sticky foods.

8. Always keep five trays in the dehydrator for circulation reasons. Check your food halfway through.

9. Vegetables are ready when they're brittle, and fruits are ready once they doesn't release any juice when squeezed.

REHYDRATING

Rehydrating dried foods allows you to use them as if they were fresh. While each food may have its own particular needs for rehydration, there are a few guidelines that will serve you well more often than not. To rehydrate fruits, cover them with boiling water and let them soak for 10 minutes. Then drain and use immediately.

Vegetables are similar. You'll add an equal ratio of vegetables and boiling water, and let them sit for between 15 minutes and three hours, depending on the food. When it's ready, use it immediately.

Having a stash of dehydrated food is a great way for you to add some variety to your diet and have easily portable snacks as well. Many foods can be dehydrated well, and while it's not recommended for you to dehydrate dairy products, you can still enjoy many dried foods. Fruits can be mixed into oatmeal. Vegetables can be used to enrich sauces. Meats can be enjoyed as jerky. With dehydration as easy as it is, there's no reason to skip it.

Chapter Summary

In this chapter, we discussed how to dehydrate and rehydrate foods.

- Dehydration removes moisture so food doesn't go moldy.
- Certain foods must be blanched, boiled, dipped, or cooked before they can be dehydrated.
- In a pinch, food can be dehydrated in the sun or the oven, but the most consistent way to do it is with a designated dehydrator.
- Rehydration is as simple as soaking foods in boiling water for prescribed amounts of time.

9

PRESERVING AND PICKLING: INTRODUCING THE FORGOTTEN ART YOUR GRANDPARENTS KNEW ALL ABOUT

I f you have a bounty of fresh berries or fruits that you need to preserve, you can do so with preserves. Likewise, a glut of cabbage or cucumbers could become a bounty of pickled foods that are tasty, healthy, and fun to snack on. Our grandparents once used these arts to protect and preserve their harvests for long after the growing season. Jams and jellies can retain up to 70% of the nutritional value of fruits, and they taste great. However, they are loaded with sugar, and you typically only eat a small amount at a time. Pickling is much more nutritionally balanced, especially if you choose methods that will ferment the foods. However, be mindful of a high salt content, as this could be detrimental to the effect you're trying to create.

THE BENEFITS OF PICKLING

Pickling offers several benefits that make it a worthwhile skill to learn in order to fill your pantry. These include:

- **Food preservation:** When you pickle food, you extend its shelf-life, especially if you don't have access to refrigerators. Pickled foods are soaked in vinegar or something of high acidity to prevent spoilage.
- **Reduced food storage cost:** While freezing is currently the most commonly used long-term storage solution for food, it is also expensive when compared to other options. Pickled food remains stable at room temperature.
- **Flavor:** Pickling was originally done to preserve food, but it also allows food to taste much better. Corned beef, for example, is pickled. Sauerkraut on a hot dog? Pickled. Kimchi? Pickled. Pickled

foods are often delicious and worth the effort you put into preparing them.

- **Health benefits:** Pickled foods, especially when they're fermented, are substantial sources of nutrients. The sodium content in the brine can also relieve muscle cramps after sweating, and boost hydration when consumed in moderation.

PICKLING METHODS

Pickling is the process of using some sort of high-acid solution (typically either vinegar or a fermented substance) to preserve food. When the environment is high in acidity, the food cannot go bad. A high acidity environment can be created through salt or vinegar.

Pickling follows just a few key steps: brining, packing in jars, covering with hot vinegar, and usually processing in a water bath. Pickled foods can then be stored somewhere cool and dark. Most often, they should be left to sit for eight weeks to develop flavor, but no one's judging if you crack into them sooner!

Pickling with Salt

Pickling with salt can be done either with dry salt or with brine. When using the dry salt method, you combine dry salt with vegetables. As the vegetables sit, the liquid is pulled out of them and creates the brine. Other times, a pre-made brine can be mixed into the vegetables to soak for a set amount of time. In this state, vegetables will ferment, which is the process during which bacteria in foods converts the sugar into lactic acid, which is a natural preservative. This is the most common method of preserving foods that usually don't process and preserve well, like cabbage, which can become kimchi or sauerkraut. Pickled foods will last for up to a year.

Pickling with Vinegar

Typically, using vinegar is a much quicker process because there's no fermentation of the vegetables. They will sit in brine for a while, which aids the flavor and crispness, before being drained, boiled in vinegar, packed in jars with more vinegar, and then water bath-canned to seal the jars. Vinegar has acetic acid, which boosts acidity and prevents microorganisms from developing.

When pickling foods, you must use very fresh ingredients or you will end up with mushy results. If you're planning on making a batch of pickled vegetables, try to pickle them as soon as they've been picked. You want to catch the food at peak freshness.

When pickling, you'll only need salt or vinegar and water. You can use both in some situations. When using salt, ensure that it is always pickling or kosher salt. These salts are free from anti-caking agents that could cause cloudiness. This isn't harmful, but it will affect the appearance. You can add other ingredients as well. Often, sugar, herbs, spices, and garlic can be added to create different varieties of flavors.

Some people choose to use firming agents for crisping up vegetables. They often turn to lime or alum. Lime is calcium hydroxide, and alum is potassium aluminum phosphate. These aren't necessary, but can be used, and you may see them in recipes from time to time.

PICKLE RECIPES

If you're interested in pickling, it's a good idea to get a recipe book to provide you with a variety of options. You can experiment with many flavor profiles, which is often welcome if you have a glut of a single vegetable. We'll go over three recipes here, but many, many others could be used.

Pickled Garlic

Pickled garlic is a great way to use up a glut of garlic. It's flavorful, and mellows out the bite garlic has while accentuating the flavor. It prolongs its shelf-life while balancing the flavors. This recipe yields 1 quart.

Ingredients

- Bay leaf (1, sliced in half)
- Cumin seeds (⅛ tsp)
- Coriander seeds (⅛ tsp)

- Crushed red chili peppers (¼ tsp, reduce if you prefer less spice)
- Peppercorns (¼ tsp)
- White wine vinegar (1¼ cup)
- Mustard seeds (⅛ tsp)
- Kosher salt (1 Tbsp)
- Garlic (4 cups, peeled)

Equipment

- Pint-sized mason jars
- Saucepan
- Spoon

Instructions

1. Wash both jars and lids in boiling water to sterilize them, then set them aside.
2. Combine vinegar, 1 cup of water, and salt in a saucepan and bring to the boil, then reduce to a low heat and cover.
3. At the bottom of each jar, layer equal amounts of each spice: peppercorns, cumin, coriander, red chili pepper, mustard seeds, and bay leaf.
4. Pack each jar with as much garlic as possible, leaving ½ inch free at the top.
5. Pour in the salt and vinegar mixture, leaving a ¼-inch headspace. Push down the garlic, and make sure bubbles are released. Clean the rims and

screw on the lids.

6. Pickle it in the refrigerator for three days, or use standard canning procedures to seal the jars.

Pickled Kimchi

Kimchi can be made simply using a handful of good ingredients. This recipe will yield several quart-sized jars, depending on how tightly you choose to pack the jars. Keep extra jars on hand, just in case.

Ingredients

- Green cabbage (1 head, cut into 1"x2" pieces with a few leaves uncut)
- Kosher salt (2 Tbsp)
- Garlic (2–3 large cloves, minced)
- Ginger (1 tsp, peeled and grated)
- Sugar (1 tsp)
- Gochugaru, Korean chili pepper (3 Tbsp)
- Green onions (4, green parts only)
- Onion (1 medium, sliced thinly)

Equipment

- Quart-sized mason jars (sterilized)
- Large bowl
- Knife and cutting board
- Wooden spoon
- Blender

Instructions

1. Begin by washing and pre-measuring all ingredients so they're ready to go.
2. Put the cabbage into a large bowl, reserving a few large leaves. Sprinkle it with salt and mix to combine. Cover the bowl and let the contents sit until wilted (between 1 and 12 hours).
3. Combine the garlic, ginger, onion, green onion, sugar, and chili pepper in the blender. Process to create a rough paste. Then check the cabbage.
4. When the cabbage is ready, drain it, reserving the liquid, and pat the leaves dry.
5. Combine the cabbage with the spice paste, mixing well.
6. Push the kimchi into jars as tightly as possible. Add liquid to each jar, leaving at least 1 inch of headspace. Water can be added if you run out of liquid to completely cover the kimchi. Push the mixture down.
7. Cover the top of each jar with one cabbage leaf. Loosely seal the jars and let them sit at room temperature for between three and five days, tasting regularly. It's done when it's sour and spicy.
8. When it's ready, remove the cabbage leaves from the top and store the jars in the fridge, tightly sealed.

Pickled Sauerkraut

Sauerkraut is created when lactobacillus, beneficial bacteria on the surface of food, ferments. This occurs when food is dipped into a brine, where the bacteria can start converting sugars into lactic acid which preserves the food. In this case, sauerkraut results from cabbage fermenting, at around 55°F, for several months. If you don't have a cellar or a cool garage, you could also store it in your fridge. The benefit is that, after the fermentation process, there will be plenty of healthy probiotics included in it.

Ingredients

- 1 head of green cabbage (roughly 3 lb)
- Kosher salt (1.5 Tbsp)
- Caraway seeds (optional, but they add flavor)

Equipment

- Canning funnel
- 2-quart canning jar (or two 1-quart mason jars)
- Mixing bowl
- Jelly jar to fit into the canning jar (or 2 if using mason jars)
- Stones, marbles, or weights to weigh down the jelly jar
- Cheesecloth
- Rubber band

Instructions

1. Begin by cleaning all your equipment. Ensure the jars are sanitized, and then wash your hands well.
2. Remove any wilted leaves around the cabbage, and cut it into quarters, trimming the core and discarding it. Then create eight wedges. Each wedge should then be sliced into thin ribbons, reminiscent of sauerkraut.
3. Put the cabbage in a bowl, and sprinkle it with salt. Use your hands to massage and squeeze the cabbage to spread the salt around. Do so for 5–10 minutes to get a consistency reminiscent of coleslaw. Then add in the caraway seeds if you're using them.
4. Pack handfuls of the cabbage into the canning jar using the funnel. Make sure you push down the cabbage from time to time to keep it packed in there.
5. Slide the jelly jar into the mouth of the canning jar, weighing it down with stones or marbles. This will keep all the cabbage weighed down and submerged in its liquid.
6. Cover the jar with cheesecloth, then secure it with a rubber band. This protects the sauerkraut from dust and insects, while also allowing for airflow.
7. Push down the cabbage every few hours for the next 24 hours to release more liquid.
8. After 24 hours, you can add more brine if the

liquid does not cover the cabbage. To do so, dissolve 1 tsp of salt in a cup of water, and pour in just enough to completely cover the cabbage.

9. Let the cabbage ferment out of sunlight and in a cool room for three to 10 days. Taste it from Day 3. When you've achieved the desired taste, you can then refrigerate it. If it begins to develop mold, skim off the moldy part and ensure the rest of the cabbage is submerged.

Chapter Summary

In this chapter, we reviewed the process of pickling to preserve foods. Key points to remember are:

- Jams and jellies preserve a lot of nutritional value, but are not very effective as they are eaten in small quantities.
- Pickling alters the flavor of a food, but is a great way to preserve its health benefits.
- Pickling can be done with salt, brine, or vinegar. When using salt or brine, fermentation occurs. When using vinegar, there is no fermentation.

10

EMERGENCY BACK UP: A NOTE ON VITAMINS AND SUPPLEMENTS

While your regular diet should be enough to provide you with all the nutritional benefits you need, it's always good to be prepared in case you can't eat as you normally would. Having vitamins and supplements means that even if you lose food, you can still keep up with the nutritional requirements of your body.

Buying vitamins isn't as straightforward as just picking up the cheapest option on the shelf, however, and you'll get what you pay for. This means that you want to buy the best, highest quality vitamins you can because cheaper options usually use subpar ingredients that may not be as easy for your body to absorb.

As you read through this chapter, we are going to address several important topics related to vitamins and supplements. First, we will discuss the best vitamins to keep and store. Then we'll address the shelf-life of various vitamins.

Finally, we'll discuss which vitamins and minerals you should prioritize.

Selecting Vitamins

Consider the various age groups that are part of your family. For example, if you have young children, make sure you have vitamins designed for younger children, as some vitamins can be overdosed on when consumed in the wrong quantities. If you have a pregnant or lactating woman in the house, have some vitamin supplements targeted to her. Women of childbearing age must have folate in higher quantities to prevent early birth defects that may occur before a woman even knows she's pregnant. Even if there are no plans to become pregnant, it may be a good idea to keep some prenatal-specific vitamins on hand, as life sometimes has its own ideas.

A complete one-a-day vitamin is usually the easiest option for each group, but you can buy vitamins individually as well. The easiest option would be to have children's one-a-day vitamins, adult vitamins, prenatal vitamins (if applicable), and senior vitamins, especially if you or anyone in your home is aging. When selecting vitamins, opt for those that are food-based. These will be most of the organic vitamins you find. However, if you can't, any vitamins are better than none.

Age-based vitamins are a significant consideration, as are sex-based ones, as people at different life stages will have different needs. In a pinch, a child should be able to take adult vitamins, but ONLY if there is no iron included. Children can get sick from iron if they get too much of it.

When selecting the type of vitamin to get, you'll notice that there are several options. You can get gummies or gels, which may be easier to take, but may not last as long as tablet or powder forms. You need to weigh longevity against taste, and in a survival or emergency situation, most people will opt for longevity over anything else.

What Is the Shelf-Life of Vitamin Supplements?

Vitamins and minerals can be stored for a sufficient period. Some may be good for up to 15 years, depending on storage, conditions, and the quality of the vitamins. If you store vitamins in a garage, where they're exposed to constantly fluctuating temperatures, they may not last nearly as long. Those stored in a pantry or a refrigerator may last longer. However, they will gradually decrease in potency as they age.

The use-by date on the vitamin packages is a suggestion. It is the point until which the potency of the vitamin stops being guaranteed. However, they may last longer than this. You can judge the shelf-life based on:

- The Vitamin: Some are more sensitive than others. Vitamin A is sensitive to light. Folic acid is stable in oxygen, but sensitive to heat and light. B12 is stable.
- Binders Added: Some binders may interact with

the vitamins, which could affect the shelf-life. Ascorbic acid, for example, is reactive because of being an acid. Most vitamins are acidic, and therefore reactive.

Shelf-life calculations are conservative. Even though your vitamins will lose potency over time, they still can provide you with plenty of benefits. To store them, keep them in their original packaging in cool, dry conditions. Make sure they are somewhere away from light, heat, oxygen, and humidity. A good idea is to place them inside a box or a light-proof container, and then place them somewhere cool. This provides several layers of protection against deterioration.

Keep in mind that while it's best to consume vitamins and supplements when recommended by the manufacturer, vitamin supplements do not go bad in the sense that they will become harmful. They will lose potency, but they will not become dangerous to your health. As long as they do not smell or look off, they should be fine.

What Vitamins Do I Need to Stock Up On?

Vitamins C and D should be prioritized for immune health, but it's good to store several others too. If possible, buy in bulk with larger bottles so you have plenty available. However, remember that just like with food, vitamins will deteriorate when exposed to heat, light, or humidity, so storage in cool, dry packages is essential. If you can keep them in a cold location, they'll remain in good condition for longer.

You want to choose pure forms in tablet or powder form to keep the vitamins at their best for as long as possible. Gelcaps have oils which will go rancid, and gummies will go bad because of moisture. Keep in mind that supplements with live bacteria (probiotics) are unlikely to keep very long, as the bacteria will die off. However, kimchi and sauerkraut, or other fermented foods, offer similar benefits to probiotic tablets.

The vitamins that are the weakest are vitamin B12 and vitamin C. For vitamin C, you could use L-ascorbic acid powder, which will remain stable for longer. One good way to store vitamins is to use a good multivitamin tablet, along with the ascorbic acid powder.

Vitamins and minerals are essential to your health, and without them, you won't feel well. In an emergency, where time is of the essence and you may need to hunt, work the land, or protect yourself, you can't risk suffering from malnutrition that can leave you ineffective. Having a stockpile of good multivitamins can help to ensure that even when food is scarce, you are nourished enough to maintain your health.

Chapter Summary

In this chapter, we reviewed the importance of supplementation and vitamins as a backup in case there is anything that prevents you from accessing a healthy diet.

- Multivitamins are the easiest way to cover all bases.
- Keep age- and sex-specific vitamins on hand according to your family's needs. Children and adults have different vitamin needs.
- In a pinch, a child can take adult vitamins that do not contain iron.
- Women of childbearing age must get enough folate to prevent birth defects should they get pregnant, so if there is a woman in the house, ensure that she has a folate-rich supplement.
- Store vitamins and minerals in a cool, dark, dry spot in their original packaging.
- The shelf life of vitamins is a conservative recommendation, and many tablets will be good for 10–15 years if stored properly.
- Vitamins B12 and C are the most fragile.
- Store vitamin C as L-ascorbic acid powder, as it is nonreactive in this form.

NOW FOR THE BEST PART!

You get to help our community by giving this book a review.

Many preppers, just like you, know how hard it is to find current, concise, and useful information, especially when starting. Not only will your review help them on their prepping journey, but the information you direct them to might also save their lives!

Do another prepper a favor and leave a review talking about the information you found, what you liked about the book, and how it helped you... even if it is just a sentence or two!

I am so very appreciative of your review, as it truly makes a difference in our community.

Thank you from the bottom of my heart for purchasing this book. I hope our paths cross again in the future.

Scan this QR code and leave a brief review on Amazon.

CONCLUSION

No one knows when disaster will strike. No one can predict when roads may be blocked, food shortages may prevent access to healthy foods, or war or catastrophic emergency may end life as we know it. We've already seen this relatively recently with the COVID-19 pandemic. No one expected that there would be something that could shut down the entire world. Yet restrictions around the world have caused shortages of many foods we once took for granted. Who's to say that next time won't be worse?

The COVID-19 pandemic was a major eye-opener for many people who never thought that anything bad could happen to them in their suburban, middle-class home, yet disaster happened. Flour and sugar were off the shelves for a while. Bread and pasta? Good luck. While shopping has returned to normal in most places, there are still echoes of shortages, and uncertainty remains: What if it happens again? Will you be prepared? Will you know what you need to keep stashed to ensure that your family will eat, no matter what happens?

Reading this book was the perfect first step to assuaging those fears, and now you've done so, you can start taking action. You've learnt everything you need to know to set up your very own food storage to prevent your family from suffering from malnutrition should anything prevent you from accessing resources normally. We live in strange and uncertain times, so being prepared is more important than ever. If you can't access food, it's your health and the health of your family that are most at risk.

Your family relies on you to ensure that they have everything they need. Your children look to you to make sure there is always food on the table. Perhaps you have a partner who relies on you too. Preparation can help you navigate difficult times and last long enough for help to arrive, or until you can start working toward self-sufficiency in other ways.

As you read through this book, you were guided through several key points to help you prepare in case another crisis hits suburbia. We went over the essentials of maintaining a healthy body, as well as the nutrients your body needs. We discussed how to keep your immune system in peak condition with the foods you choose. From there, we discussed several game plans to stock up your pantry with confidence. From shopping trips to stock up the pantry to gardening your way towards self-sufficiency, we explored ways to ensure that food will be available if disaster strikes.

We also discussed several storage options to help you keep your food for as long as possible. We discussed the best methods for dry storage in the pantry to keep your food from rotting, from being infested with insects or rodents, and from losing flavor. We discussed how to can to maintain nutrition, and how to do so safely to prevent botulism. We went over stocking a chest freezer and how to keep it functioning for as long as possible. We addressed dehydration as an alternate method to store foods long-term. We went over how to pickle vegetables that may otherwise not preserve well. And finally, we discussed a game plan for stocking up on vitamins that will ensure that no matter what the situation, you and your family will have essential nutrients.

You have all the tools at your disposal at this point. You know what you need, how you can get it, and how it can all be kept and stored to ensure that it's there when you need it. What happens from here is up to you. Aim for a stockpile of food to last you and your family three to six months, by which time, you should be able to stabilize and find alternative sources of food if necessary. You owe it to yourself to be prepared, and now you are.

Thank you for taking the time to read through this book as your introduction to creating your very own stockpile of food. Hopefully, as you read, you found plenty of information that was useful to you. Hopefully, you feel a bit more at ease that even if disaster strikes, you can still get by if you know what you're doing. You've got the knowledge. You can learn the skills. And then you'll survive.

If you feel more confident, please consider leaving your thoughts and feelings in a review to spread the word and help others prepare as well.

The human species is incredibly adaptable. It's versatile. It can survive in just about any environment. You can do this too if you put your mind to it. You already have the mindset of prepping. Now it's about implementation.

T.Riley

A Special Gift to My Readers

Included with your purchase of this book is your free
copy of the *Emergency Information Planner*

Follow the link below to receive your copy:
www.tedrileyauthor.com
Or by accessing the QR code:

Scan me

You can also join our Facebook community **Suburban
Prepping with Ted**, or contact me directly via
ted@tedrileyauthor.com.

REFERENCES

Bellew, P. (2016, March 21). *33 Essential Foods to Stock Pile.* Ask a Prepper. https://www.askaprepper.com/33-essential-foods-to-stock-pile/

Better Health Channel. (n.d.). *Immune System Explained.* https://www.betterhealth.vic.gov.au/health/conditionsandtreatments/immune-system

Biggers, S. (2021, May 24). *The Best Vitamins and Supplements for Hard Times.* Backdoor Survival. https://www.backdoorsurvival.com/the-best-vitamins-and-supplements-for-hard-times/

Bone, E. (2013, December 13). *Food Preservation Techniques: Learn How to Pickle.* The Prepper Journal. https://www.theprepperjournal.com/2013/10/11/food-preservation-techniques-learn-pickle/

Bradford, A. (2018, July 26). *Upright Freezer or Chest Freezer: Which Should You Buy?* CNET. https://www.cnet.com/how-to/upright-freezer-vs-chest-freezer/

Brown, C. (2020, January 9). *Common Home Preservation Methods: Advantages and Disadvantages.* Delishably. https://delishably.com/sauces-preserves/homepreservationadvantagesanddisadvantages pt2

Burgess, L. (2018, July 10). *The Best Foods for Boosting Your Immune System.* Medical News Today. https://www.medicalnewstoday.com/articles/322412#which-foods-boost-the-immune-system

Carter, B. (n.d.). *DIY Dehydrated-Foods Guide.* US Preppers. https://uspreppers.com/diy-dehydrated-foods-guide/

Childs, C., Calder, P., & Miles, E. (2019, August 16). Diet and Immune Function. *Nutrients, 11(8), 1933.* https://doi.org/10.3390/nu11081933

Christensen, E. (2020, January 29). *How to Make Homemade Sauerkraut in a Mason Jar.* Kitchn. https://www.thekitchn.com/how-to-make-homemade-sauerkraut-in-a-mason-jar-193124

Clay, J. (1992, August/September). *Home Canning for Beginners: How to Can Your Food Year-Round.* Mother Earth News. https://www.motherearthnews.com/real-food/home-canning-for-beginners-zmaz92aszshe

David, N. (2018, February 28). *Frozen Food Storage*. PrepersSurvive. http://www.prepperssurvive.com/frozen-food-storage/

Grey, S. (2019, January 10). *The Advantages of Pickling Foods*. Our Everyday Life. https://oureverydaylife.com/548285-the-advantages-of-pickling-foods.html

Gunnars, K. (2018, September 5). *10 Surprising Health Benefits of Honey*. Healthline. https://www.healthline.com/nutrition/10-benefits-of-honey#section10

Gunnars, K. (2021, April 8). *6 Health Benefits of Apple Cider Vinegar, Backed by Science*. Healthline. https://www.healthline.com/nutrition/6-proven-health-benefits-of-apple-cider-vinegar

Hanus, R. (2013, December 12). *The 5 Minute Prepper #15: Make Freezing Part of Your Food Storage*. The Grow Network. https://thegrownetwork.com/the-5-minute-prepper-15-make-freezing-part-of-your-food-storage/

HappyPreppers.com. (n.d.). *How to Dehydrate Foods*. https://www.happypreppers.com/Dehydrating.html

HappyPreppers.com. (n.d.). *Super Immunity Boosters*. https://www.happypreppers.com/immunity.html

Harvard Health Publishing. (2021, February 15) *How to Boost Your Immune System*. https://www.health.harvard.edu/staying-healthy/how-to-boost-your-immune-system

Healthy Canning. (2020, July 19). *Canning Vegetables.* https://www.healthycanning.com/canning-vegetables/

Henry, P. (2013, February 16). *Prepping 101—Prepper Food Storage.* The Prepper Journal. https://www.theprepperjournal.com/2013/02/16/prepper-101-food-preps-30-days-worth-of-food/

Higgs, J. (2019, July 15). *How to Store Food for Long Term Storage in Case of Emergency.* Caltex Plastics. https://caltexplastics.com/store-food-longterm.html

Jones, K. (2019, December 17). *Shelf-Life of Vitamin Supplements in a Survival Food Supply.* The Provident Prepper. https://theprovidentprepper.org/shelf-life-of-vitamin-supplements-in-a-survival-food-supply/

Jones, K. (2021, February 04). *Long Term Food Storage: Best Containers and Treatment Methods.* The Provident Prepper. https://theprovidentprepper.org/long-term-food-storage-best-containers-and-treatment-methods/

Jorgustin, K. (2018, December 14). *Survival Vitamins and Supplements.* Modern Survival Blog. https://modernsurvivalblog.com/preps/survival-prep-vitamins-and-medications/

Just in Case Jack. (2016, July 19). *Emergency Food Storage: How to Build Your Survival Food System.* Skilled Survival. https://www.skilledsurvival.com/emergency-food-supply-how-to-get-started/

Kubala, J (2021, June 24). *The Definitive Guide to Healthy Eating in Real Life.* Healthline. https://www.healthline.com/nutrition/how-to-eat-healthy-guide

Lehman, S. (2021, February 08). *The Basics of a Healthy, Balanced Diet.* Verywell Fit. https://www.verywellfit.com/the-basics-of-a-healthy-balanced-diet-2506675

Matheny, M. (2016, August 20). *Easy Pickled Garlic: For Refrigerating or Canning.* The Yummy Life. https://www.theyummylife.com/Pickled_Garlic

McClellan, M. (2019, October 10). *A Beginner's Guide to Canning.* Serious Eats. https://www.seriouseats.com/2012/02/how-to-can-canning-pickling-preserving-ball-jars-materials-siphoning-recipes.html

McIntosh, J. (2019, October 9). *Everything You Need to Know about Eggs.* Medical News Today. https://www.medicalnewstoday.com/articles/283659

McMordie, K. (2018, August 29). *Beginner's Guide to Canning.* Lively Table. https://livelytable.com/beginners-guide-to-canning/

Mitchell, C. (n.d.). *Experts Explain Which Foods You Should Stockpile before Dealing with a Natural Disaster.* Accu-Weather. https://www.accuweather.com/en/weather-news/experts-explain-which-foods-you-should-stockpile-before-dealing-with-a-natural-disaster-2/432899

Newcomer, L. (2013, May 21). *Hot and Healthy: How to Make Better Kimchi at Home.* Greatist. https://greatist.com/health/how-to-make-your-own-diy-kimchi

Nick, J. (2021, February 18). *7 Ways You Can Make Your Garlic Last Longer.* Good Housekeeping. https://www.goodhousekeeping.com/food-recipes/a20707233/how-to-store-garlic/

Pierce, R. (2019, August 15). *The Ultimate List of What You Can (and Cannot!) Can.* J&R Pierce Family Farm. https://jrpiercefamilyfarm.com/2019/08/15/the-ultimate-list-of-what-you-can-and-cannot-can/

Powitz, R. (2005, June 1). *7 Simple Rules for Effective and Hygienic Dry Goods Storage.* Food Safety Magazine. https://www.foodsafetymagazine.com/magazine-archive1/junejuly-2005/7-simple-rules-for-effective-and-hygienic-dry-goods-storage/

Ready. (n.d.). *Food.* https://www.ready.gov/food

RecipeTips. (n.d.). *Canning Temperatures and Processing Times.* https://www.recipetips.com/kitchen-tips/t--1396/canning-temperatures-and-processing-times.asp

Russell, P. (2016, December 6). *A Beginner's Guide to Canning at Home.* Instructables. https://www.instructables.com/A-Beginners-Guide-to-Canning-at-Home/

Schend, J. (2020, April 30). *15 Foods That Boost the Immune System*. Healthline. https://www.healthline.com/health/food-nutrition/foods-that-boost-the-immune-system

Science Daily. (2019, September 04). *Many Older Adults Aren't Fully Prepared for Emergency Situations, Poll Finds*. https://www.sciencedaily.com/releases/2019/09/190904081313.htm

Spurr, T. (2015, October 14). *Blackberry Jam. Full of Goodness or a "Devil's Food"?* Eat Yourself Brilliant. http://www.eatyourselfbrilliant.co.uk/blackberry-jam-full-of-goodness-or-a-devils-food/

Stone, K. (2018, November 27). *How to Dehydrate Food for Beginners*. Stone Family Farmstead. https://stonefamilyfarmstead.com/how-to-dehydrate-food/

Szalay, J. (2015, December 10). *What Is Protein?* Live Science. https://www.livescience.com/53044-protein.html

Szalay, J. (2015, December 18). *What Is Dietary Fat?* Live Science. https://www.livescience.com/53145-dietary-fat.html

Szalay, J. (2017, July 14). *What Are Carbohydrates?* Live Science. https://www.livescience.com/51976-carbohydrates.html

U.S. Food and Drug Administration (n.d.). *Nutrition Facts Labeling Requirements.* https://www.fda.gov/media/99069/download

Made in the USA
Middletown, DE
11 September 2023

38337752R00210